Contents

EVERYTHING IN ORDER: SEQUENCING EXERCISES

LEONARDO WHO? ARTISTIC EXPRESSIONS

FOLLOWING THE GOLDEN RULE: HELPING OTHERS

NEVER FAR AWAY: KEEPING IN TOUCH

GIVING BACK: COMMUNITY INVOLVEMENT

INFORMATIONAL CD

Preface

We at the Myers Research Institute of Menorah Park Center for Senior Living take great pleasure in presenting this manual to you. When we first started writing, our thoughts were focused on residents in nursing homes with dementia and their family members who come to visit them. Over time, we realized that these kinds of activities also could help families who are caring for persons with dementia in their homes. A visit is a visit. These activities work very well in many different settings.

This manual was created to help people have, as the title says, a different visit with relatives who have memory problems, such as those related to dementia. While we have written other manuals for helping people with dementia (see our website at www.myersresearch.org), this manual is special. This time we are writing specifically to you – all those who love their family members dearly, but need some ideas or inspiration for how to better engage and interact with them.

We ask you to pardon the informality in our writing, but we wanted to make this manual entertaining as well as informative. Please read through our activity suggestions and try them out. We understand that every person with dementia is different. What works for one person may not work for another, and what works one day may not work another day. However, we hope that here you can find many activities that are right for you and your family member regardless of where they are in the course of dementia. The more of these you try, the easier it will be to start coming up with your own activities, too.

This manual is a result of a grant to the Menorah Park Center for Senior Living from the national Alzheimer's Association. Cameron J. Camp, Ph.D., Director of the Myers Research Institute, was the principal investigator of the project. Miriam Rose and Adena Joltin served as project manager at different points in time. The purpose of the grant was to design activities for family members to use when visiting relatives in long-term care, and to document the effects of family visitors using these activities. The activities are based on principles of Montessori-Based Dementia Programming™, which was developed at Menorah Park. We describe this approach to creating activities in the Introduction to this manual. Almost all of the activities contained in this manual were used by family members during our study. A few activities were used in other related studies at Menorah Park, or have been inspired by activities that we used in our research. All of these activities have been reviewed by the Director of Activities at Menorah Park, Pam Nicholson, B.A., M.Div., and by staff of the Cleveland Chapter of the Alzheimer's Association, most notably Marty Kelly, LSW.

We consider ourselves very fortunate to have had the opportunity to work with so many wonderful families during our project. They have amazed and inspired us with their courage, wisdom, and joy. Our hope is that this book can give a little something back to other families facing similar challenges.

Find activities that are right for you and your family member.

Introduction

As we mentioned in the Preface, this is a type of "how-to" manual for having a different, better visit with a person who has memory impairment. For many people, this means visiting a person in a nursing home or in assisted living. What is such a visit typically like? Usually, when you visit your family member or loved one, they are already dressed. They probably have already eaten breakfast, brushed their teeth, and taken their medications. Before they lived in a facility, providing physical care for your loved one may have been the focus of your interactions with them. Conversations surrounded taking their morning meds or eating their breakfast. What do you talk about now? How do you have a meaningful visit with someone if they have difficulty remembering the past, or if verbal communication is limited?

When the person with memory impairment lives at home, with you or in their own apartment or house, similar challenges arise. It is so hard, sometimes, not to think about the person they were—to focus on what has been lost. What do you tell your friends or your loved one's friends who come to visit? What guidance can you give relatives from out of town who may not realize what it's like to live with and interact with your loved one? How can you explain or demonstrate what to do and what not to do?

Providing care involves more than physical care. Even for a relative in a nursing home, the caregiving role for you does not truly conclude; it just changes. You are now delivering care in the form of visits instead of medications. Meaningful, engaging visits are an important part of daily living for your relative with memory impairment, wherever they live. If they cannot remember the details of the visit, it is not really important. The positive feelings they have because of a good visit can linger afterwards, for them and for you. You both want to look forward to the next visit. Let's talk about how to make this happen.

Positive feelings because of a good visit can linger.

FINDING THE INDIVIDUAL

When dealing with a person who has memory deficits because of dementia or other problems, we have to keep something critical in mind: they are still a person. Our responsibility is to connect with and bring out this person by finding ways around their problems. If conversation is not an option during a visit, take the focus off of conversation. Try doing something instead, such as an activity. Activities serve a much greater function than just making it easier to have a visit. They allow us to rediscover the person who is hidden by the deficits.

You may think about your mother or father or relative and wonder how exactly you could do an activity with them? They may not remember much, they may be in a wheelchair, or they may have Parkinson's disease coupled with dementia. How could this possibly work? What could they do?

The first and most important step is to focus your thinking on what abilities and interests they still have. Do they still read? Can they still talk? Can they point? Can they hold things? Do they still walk independently? Can they answer questions? What did they do for a living? Did they have siblings? What did they enjoy doing most? Did they ever travel? Instead of concentrating solely on their limitations, it is critical to find their remaining strengths and build off of those.

The second key to an engaging visit is all in the approach. Activities, in general, could help to make a visit go more smoothly. The main thing to remember is that there is no "right" way or "wrong" way to do these activities. The only thing that is important is allowing your family member to feel good about your visit and themselves. If they are happy afterwards, it was a good activity and a good visit. If they are not, then no matter how many things were made or how much work was accomplished during the visit, the activity needs to be changed or replaced.

MONTESSORI-BASED PRINCIPLES

At the Myers Research Institute, we've developed a way of making and presenting activities for persons with memory impairments. Our focus is on working with strengths and abilities that remain, finding the person behind the memory problems, engaging the individual, and letting everyone involved feel good about the experience. It is called Montessori-Based Dementia Programming™.

This approach is based on the work of Maria Montessori, a physician in Italy working in the early part of the 20th century. She called her approach "The Montessori Method." This method was originally used with disadvantaged children to provide them with opportunities to meaningfully interact with their environments. Adapting this approach to fit older adults with memory impairments results in meaningful activities to enhance the quality of visits. Here are some examples of guiding principles we use when designing activities using Montessori-Based Dementia Programming™:

- Try to include materials that can be manipulated.

- Use materials that give hints or guidance to the person with memory impairment.

Find remaining strengths and build off of those.

Additional information is available on the CD included in this manual.

- Use materials that are free of background clutter.

- Match a task to the ability of the person with memory impairment. For example, printed material should be in a large, sans serif type size (e.g., 48 pt. Arial font).

- Try to keep the room quiet and the place where you are working free of clutter during activities.

- Give choices to the person with memory impairment whenever possible. For example, you might begin with an invitation, such as "Would you like to try *this* or *this*?"

- Refrain from repeatedly correcting the person with memory impairment.

- Always demonstrate what you want a person to do before asking them to do it.

- Remember that persons with memory impairments can sometimes improve with practice, even if they don't know that they tried something before. For example, they may get better at reading after trying a page or two. If at first they have difficulties, it's okay to try again. Just be sure to avoid any frustration.

It may take a few tries before you find an activity that they really relate to. A good way to find out what they like doing is to ask, after doing an activity, "Would you like to do this again sometime? Would you like to do something else?" This gives them a chance to make a choice, and their answer can give you guidance as to their likes and dislikes.

More information about Montessori-Based Dementia Programming™, along with a list of references, and additional sources of useful information, are included on the CD in this manual. Please look over the information, and contact us if you have any questions about using the activities or resources we have described in this manual.

How to Use This Manual

When using this manual, it is important to keep a few things in mind. First, the information that we present on these pages should just be a starting point for you. We wanted this to serve as a springboard in a sense, just a beginning for you to take some ideas and run with them. We understand that every activity may not work the way we described it. We expect that. People have their own unique interests and abilities. That is why adaptation and individualization are keys for any type of activity, regardless of the approach that you follow. Take our ideas and transform them into activities that work for your loved one. Individualize these activities. If we present an idea that involves flowers, but you think that flags would appeal more to your loved one, use flags. Change these activities however you need to make them work for you. Adapt and modify!

Second, here are guidelines to help create activities that will let your family member feel good about themselves.

- Embrace the idea that there is no wrong answer.

- Give hints on how to do an activity while it is being done.

- Walk your family member through every step.

- Give your family member answers.

- Avoid correcting your family member if you think a mistake is made.

- If an activity is too challenging, make the activity less complex.

- Do the activity together.

- Do the activity first while your family member watches.

- Provide a demonstration for your loved one to help them.

Change activities to make them work for you and your loved one.

Finally, monitor the emotional status of your family member during an activity. If your loved one is having a bad day, and they tell you they don't want to do something, save it for another day. If they become upset during an activity, change it or stop. We would not want them to associate an activity with any negativity. The purpose of an activity is to let you and your family member feel good about what you have done.

CATEGORIES

You may notice that all of our activities are grouped according to activity categories, such as sorting and matching, games and puzzles, etc. There are a number of other ways that we could have categorized, such as by gender or functioning level. However, we did not want to deter anyone from trying an activity because it was classified as a "male" activity or a "high functioning" activity. All activities should be adapted to fit your loved one's needs.

LANGUAGE

As we explained in our preface, our goal was to create a manual that was fun as well as informative. Therefore, our language is a bit informal. For example, we use "they" rather than he/she when referring to your loved one. Also, we use contractions to make the language more conversational.

Templates help guide your family member.

You will hear the word "Template" throughout this entire manual. Allow us to explain. A template is something that you create for an activity that helps guide your family member. Templates give every piece of an activity a place to be placed. Let's say, for example, that you and your loved one were doing an activity with different-sized measuring spoons, and the purpose of the activity was for your loved one to organize the spoons from largest to smallest. We would create a template for this activity by outlining the shape of each measuring spoon on a piece of paper, going from largest to smallest. This gives your family member a visual guide. They can see by looking at your template that there is a spot for every spoon. They can hold each spoon up to the different outlines to help them decide which spoon goes where. When the spoons have all been placed on outlines, they can see that the activity has been completed. Whenever we have an opportunity to make a template, we do it.

LAYOUT

Each activity starts with a **DESCRIPTION** section, which has a few sentences to introduce you to the activity. All of the descriptions are brief, so if you read a description and are not sure that the activity fits your loved one, read on a bit before ruling it out. There are always adaptations that can be made, so be sure to keep an open and creative mind.

The **HOW TO** section is our description of how we would do or set up the activity. That doesn't mean that our suggestions are the only way, or the right way, for your family member. They may have special needs or require things to be set up or carried out differently. This brings us back to the whole idea of adaptation and modification. Read the "How To" section, but do not be limited by it.

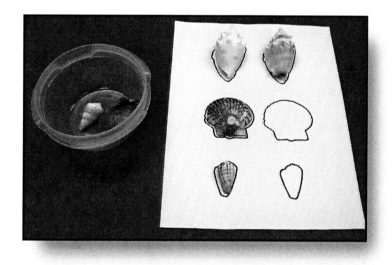

The **TIPS** section lists suggestions that we have picked up along the way when we, too, have had to make adaptations. The important thing is to keep trying.

The **ADAPTATIONS** section is important because we give alternatives for each activity. This is why we suggest reading through the entire explanation of an activity before ruling it out. Perhaps the activity may not work for your loved one as it is first described, but one of the listed adaptations may work. Or, reading this section may give you your own ideas for how to adapt the same activity.

The important thing is to keep trying.

IMPORTANT WARNING:

Certain activities outlined in this manual involve the use of materials that, without adequate supervision, might endanger a person with memory impairment. Before you give these materials to persons with memory impairments, be sure to describe the materials and demonstrate their use to them. Always use non-toxic materials.

Sometimes persons with memory impairments caused by dementia or other problems may become confused and place small objects in their mouths.

They also may try to taste paint, glue, or other supplies used when making activities. Those with memory impairments should be closely supervised while engaging in these activities.

Myers Research Institute of Menorah Park Center for Senior Living and its affiliates will not be liable for injury or damages caused by the materials or failure of the participants to use the materials or conduct the activities as indicated in these instructions.

Fabrics & Wallpaper

DESCRIPTION

This activity is for all the designers or décor connoisseurs in the group! The purpose of this activity is to take a trip back in time with your loved one and allow them to let those decorating juices flow once again. Fabric and wallpaper remnants are presented to your family member and they are to match the fabrics and the wallpaper swatches that coordinate the best, in their opinion.

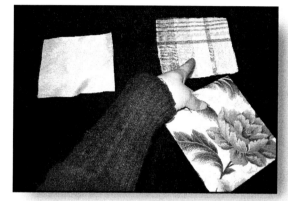

HOW TO

Take a trip back in time with your loved one.

1. The first step to creating this activity is to begin your search for remnants. Your quickest route to finding remnants may be an interior design studio. They will definitely have remnants of both fabric and wallpaper, and may even have a collection of old sample books. A big collection that may be stashed away in some storage closet, and donating one of these books to you may very well be welcomed! If you cannot visit an interior design studio, a fabric store would obviously have fabric remnants and a hardware or paint store would have wallpaper. Be sure to ask if there are any remnants for sale. The idea is not to spend hundreds of dollars purchasing several rolls of wallpaper and yards of fabric. Look for a variety of swatches, but be sure that you get some wallpaper-fabric combos that match in an obvious way, such as color. If your family member gets fancy and wants to mix and match patterns, that's great. However, it is important to have some more obvious color-coordinated matches available in case they have difficulty matching patterns.

2. Once you have a collection of wallpaper and fabrics, cut them into nice size squares to neaten them up a bit. We do not want threads hanging from the fabric and the wallpaper to have really jagged edges. This can be distracting.

Engage loved ones in activities that pertain to their interests.

3. Begin the activity by handing your family member a wallpaper swatch. While they are holding the wallpaper, you can present them with two fabric choices. Ask them to point to the fabric choice that coordinates best with the wallpaper that they are holding. If they choose a match, then you can discuss it. Ask them what they like about it or if they see that particular combo working well in a living room or a den.

4. If they do not see a match, continue showing them fabric swatches, only two at a time. We would not go with more than ten total fabric options (presented in pairs of two, equaling five pairs) at any given time. This way you are presenting, at the most, five sets of fabric swatches. If they do not think that any of the fabrics match by the time that you have shown all ten, then that's fine too. Move on to another wallpaper selection. It is also important to not overwhelm them with the number of matches you are asking them to make. Therefore, we would suggest only asking them to find a fabric match for a total of five wallpaper swatches. This number would depend on how long the process is taking. If there is a lot of reminiscing going on in between each match, that is wonderful. Possibly you only get through two swatches.

5. Continue following this process. Show two fabric swatches at a time, but stop after you have shown five different pairs. Also, only present a total of five wallpaper swatches to coordinate, at the most. We do not want to overwhelm them with too many choices. You can always come back and do more later.

TIPS

- Our idea is to use fabrics and wallpaper, but possibly you may want to use paint sample cards (available free of charge at most paint stores) instead of the wallpaper. Change the activity however you want. Our suggestions can simply be starting points for you.

- Ignore the mismatch! If your family member comes up with a crazy fabric-wallpaper combo, it is perfectly acceptable. Keep reminding yourself of the purpose: *engagement.*

- Another important suggestion is to refrain from asking any questions about specific names of patterns. If your family member is experiencing any difficulties with their memory, they may not be able to tell you that plaid is called "plaid." It is best not to risk having them feel bad about their answer.

- It is important to remember that modern contemporary style may not appeal to your family member, and that is understandable. However, differences between modern and traditional designs can become a topic of discussion.

- A final tip is to keep an open mind about this activity. Even if you cannot get to an interior design, fabric, or hardware store, you can just as easily do the same activity with pictures. It is great when you can have "real" materials to use for activities, but we understand that this is not always practical. Collect pictures of wallpaper patterns and pictures of fabrics. Follow the same approach as discussed above. You will still be engaging them in an activity that pertains to their interests and that they will enjoy.

Keep reminding yourself of the purpose: ENGAGEMENT.

ADAPTATIONS

More Challenging

- To make this activity more challenging, you can add an additional component to your match. How about some furniture? Collect some pictures of furniture pieces and have your family member coordinate the fabric, wallpaper, and furniture.

- Another suggestion is to create a room portfolio, just as you see in the design shows! The designers present their potential clients with a poster that includes fabric swatches, paint samples, wallpaper, rug pieces, furniture pictures, etc. All of the swatches and samples on the poster board are the items that the designer would use to redecorate a room in the client's home. Make a portfolio with your family member. This could be a fun project that would increase the challenge of this activity and spread it across several days and even weeks.

Coordinate swatches yourself and ask for opinions about your matches.

Less Challenging

- To make this activity less challenging, you can eliminate the idea of coordinating the wallpaper with fabric swatches, and instead sort into two categories: Wallpaper and Fabric. You would show your family member a mixture of fabric and wallpaper swatches and they would have to determine whether the swatch you were showing them was fabric or wallpaper. You should create labels that say "Wallpaper" and "Fabric" so they could place the swatch under the correct label.

- You can also do a sort between likes and dislikes. Your family member would still be shown different swatches, but they would just sort between which swatches they liked, and which they disliked.

- You can also use textured fabrics, such as velvet, brocade and corduroy, and just focus on the sense of touch. Pieces of fabric can be matched according to their textures or you can simply present fabrics and let your family member feel the textures for themselves. Do whatever they enjoy.

- And finally, you could also coordinate the swatches yourself in front of your family member, and ask their opinion about your matches.

Card Sort

DESCRIPTION

This activity is for the card sharks out there! Do you remember the first card game you played? Was it playing 52 Pickup with an older sibling or a game of Crazy Eights with your parents? At some point you may have even moved to the high stakes game of poker, including trips to Vegas. This next activity serves as a reminder of your family member's card playing days. The stakes are not as high, but this card sorting game will hopefully keep your family member on their toes.

HOW TO

1. The main idea behind this activity is suit sorting, so you will need a regular deck of cards.

2. On the two pages following this activity description, you will find four card figures. You can create templates by cutting out each of these and coloring in the suit symbols (spade, heart, club, and diamond).

3. The idea is to match a card from the deck with the corresponding suit on the template. Demonstrate for your family member before you ask them to do it. After demonstrating, let them choose a playing card and place it on the template.

TIPS

- Begin with a partial deck of cards. You can add more as your family member becomes familiar with the activity.

- If your family member is visually impaired, there are jumbo decks of cards for those with low vision. You can often find them at dollar stores or other stores that sell playing cards.

- There are other decks of cards especially constructed for persons who have difficulty holding regular-sized cards.

- You may have to modify your template to accommodate special cards.

Do you remember the first card game you played?

ADAPTATIONS

More Challenging

- Create the templates together with your loved one.

- Put the cards in a sequence.

- You can try a different card sorting activity without a template. Rather than sorting by suit, you could try grouping all the like numbers together. All of the sevens could be together in a pile; all of the queens would be together, etc.

- Play a card game such as War, Go-Fish, Gin Rummy, or Blackjack.

- Have your family member match a poker hand with a label that corresponds with it, such as "Flush" or "Straight."

Less Challenging

- Sort only a few cards instead of several. You can use only one or two if you want. You can always try again later or increase the number with practice.

- You can sort simply by color. Instead of any structured template, take a piece of red and a piece of black construction paper. Have your family member select one card from the deck and place it either on the red paper or the black paper depending on the color of the suit.

- Get two decks of cards that have different backings. Mix the decks together and have your family member separate the decks.

- Instead of sorting all four suits, sort only two suits. Use only one page of the template. Give your family member only the cards that correspond with those two suits.

- Your loved one can have a designated helper. This could be a wonderful interaction for a grandchild and a grandparent.

This could be a wonderful interaction for a grandchild and a grandparent.

Card Sort Template Page 1

Cut out the templates and color in the suit symbols. Your loved one can help!

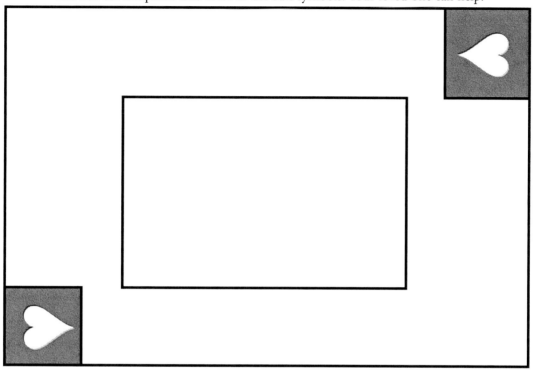

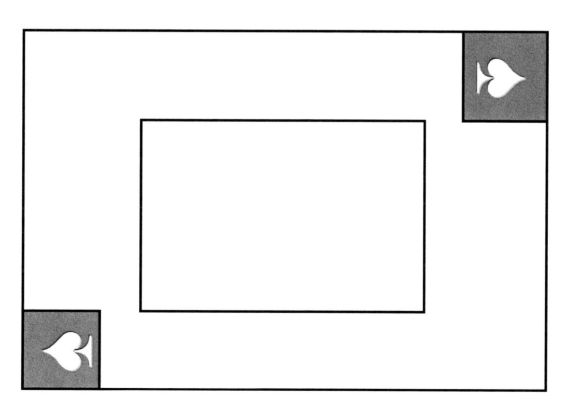

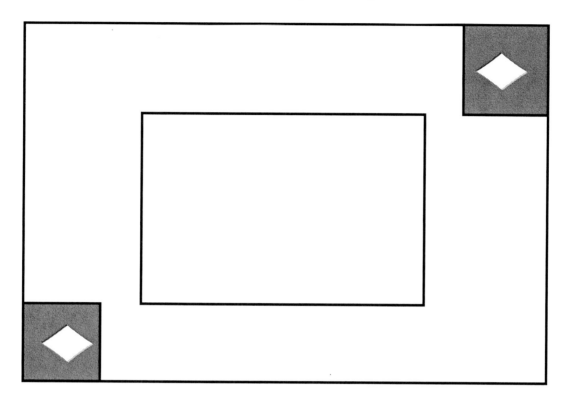

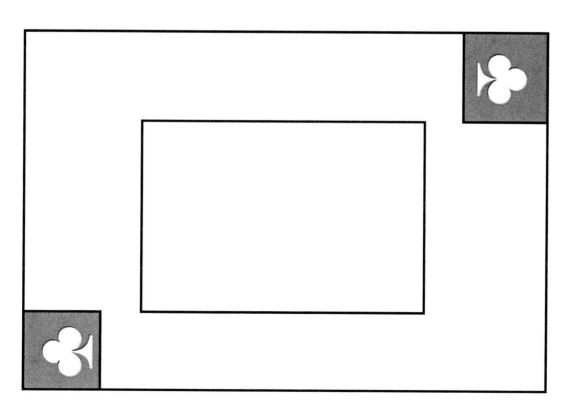

Seashell Match

DESCRIPTION

If the beach is too far from home, this matching activity can possibly serve as a pleasant reminder. Seashell pairs are outlined on a template. The focus of the activity is on matching the pairs using the template as a guide.

HOW TO

1. To make a seashell match, you need to get some seashells and a container for them. You can go to most craft stores and purchase bags or baskets of seashells and pick out pairs from them. Shells have also been spotted at many dollar stores. You need to ensure that the seashell pairs are different from one another. It would be ideal if each pair were distinguishable in terms of shape and color. Don't include too many pairs at the start. It's better to add pairs as they get used to the activity.

2. Once you have selected your seashell pairs, create your template. You can use a variety of materials: a large sheet of construction paper, cardstock, felt, foam sheets, etc. Take a permanent marker and outline each pair of seashells on your template. Make sure that the two shells that make up each individual pair are clearly next to each other and enough space is in-between every pair (see photo above).

Provide something that is enjoyable and engaging.

TIPS

*   To add additional cueing for this activity, you can add some color. Put colored dot stickers on the back of the seashells (each pair has its own color) and place coordinating colored dots on the template as well. You can purchase these colored dots at most places that have an office supply aisle.

*   If the matching is creating any difficulty, provide assistance. Our goal is not to complete the activity the "right" way, it is to provide something that is enjoyable and engaging.

- If there is any confusion or hesitation encountered initially, eliminate the idea of matching altogether. One of the great things about Montessori-Based activities is that they can be altered. Just look at the different seashells together instead of trying to match them up. If your family member enjoys just looking at the shells or holding them in their hands, that's engaging as well! Perhaps it will turn into a reminiscing activity and lead to talking about family vacations at the beach.

ADAPTATIONS

More Challenging

- If you like the idea of the seashell match, but this activity doesn't provide enough of a challenge for your family member, eliminate the template. Have your loved one match up the seashells without any template or color-coded cues.

- Or, add more pairs to match up. This increases the complexity as well.

- You could also create a matching game: names of creatures and their shells.

Less Challenging

- It may help to let your family member watch you place one of each shell pair on the template and then ask your family member to find a match for each pair, one shell at a time.

- To make the activity a bit less challenging, reduce the number of shell pairs. If you need to, only do a match of one pair! Outline one seashell and have your family member find the match to that one seashell.

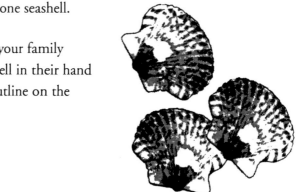

- Or, you can have your family member hold a shell in their hand and point to its outline on the template.

Just looking at the shells or holding them is engaging as well!

Purse/Shoe Match

DESCRIPTION

The purse/shoe match allows your family member to enjoy an aspect of shopping all over again. This activity consists of matching purses with coordinating shoes.

HOW TO

1. You can use actual purses and shoes. If real shoes and purses are an option for you, start gathering. Look in your closet. Look in your friends' closets. Possibly you can hit the local thrift store so you can expand your collection without spending a lot of money. Try to gather a variety and attempt to create some matches on your own. For example, if you find a purse with brown in it, try to find a pair of brown shoes as well. The fashion-minded (meaning your family member) may see different connections and match purses and shoes differently than the average person, but that is perfectly acceptable. There is no right or wrong with a Montessori-Based approach, and we never want to discourage expressions of individuality. But having some more obvious color matching options available is good in case your family member can only see the more obvious relationships.

   If gathering the real thing is not a practical option for you, just search for pictures of purses and shoes. Cut them out of magazines or store catalogs. Follow the same procedure as described above. Find a variety and attempt to match them in some way in your own mind.

Spark some conversation about those good old shopping trips.

2. Once you feel that you have a nice collection, you can begin. Start by showing your family member one shoe. Have them hold onto the shoe (or picture) and you can show them two different purses (or pictures) at a time. "Do you think that either of these purses would match this shoe?" If the response is "no," continue to show only two new purse selections at a time. As always, we do not want to overwhelm with too many selections. If the response is "yes," you can talk a bit about why they match well or ask your family member if they would ever wear that particular purse/shoe duo. If your family member does not seem particularly interested in conversation about the purse and shoes, you can try another shoe. Repeat the process of only displaying two purse selections at a time.

3. Perhaps an activity such as this truly will spark some conversation about those good old shopping trips that you loved so much. If so, great! The object is not to make as many matches as you can, but to engage your family member in an activity that is hopefully tapping into an interest. If the activity becomes a reminiscing activity and you make only one match or do not even get to matching, you still will share an extremely positive and meaningful experience together. Is there any better experience than sharing some quality time with a loved one?

TIPS

- The best tip for this or any activity is to simply avoid correcting. There is no right or wrong. If your family member matches a purple and yellow polka-dot purse with a black zebra print shoe, who is harmed? It is fine to allow them to think that this is an accessory match made in heaven!

ADAPTATIONS

More Challenging

- Instead of handing your family member a shoe and having them select between two purse choices for a match, hand them a basket with two purses and two pairs of shoes in it, and let them coordinate.

- If two sets do not increase the challenge enough, increase the number of sets. Once again, it is better to start off simple and increase if needed. If you're working with pictures, do the same thing. Hand your family member two sets of pictures and have them match up pairs.

- Another way to make this activity a bit more challenging is to add another dimension to the match. Make this a shoe/purse/belt match instead. Now your family member is matching three things at once. If you attempt the three-dimensional match, start off slow.

Less Challenging

- Make it a show-and-tell activity. Show your family member your collection. Give them one shoe at a time to hold, and tell them a story about each one. These do not necessarily have to be entirely true stories! Tell them where you think you could wear it, how you got it for a great bargain, or what type of outfit you think would go with each shoe and purse.

- Match them up yourself. Show your loved one what you think matches. Always remember, the point is engagement and enjoyment.

Is there any better experience than sharing some quality time with a loved one?

Face Puzzle

DESCRIPTION

Face puzzles are exactly that—puzzles made out of photos of faces! It's fun to do this activity, especially when the photo is of someone that is important to you or your family member.

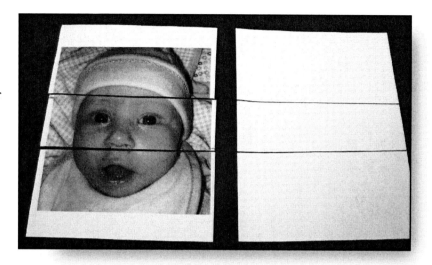

HOW TO

1. Select a picture. It can be a photo of a family member or a picture from a magazine. (You could even use a photo of a favorite pet or an object relating to their career if you want to use something other than faces). The picture should be large (8.5 x 11 should work well), so it may have to be enlarged.

2. Glue the enlarged picture onto a piece of cardstock or poster board before cutting out the pieces. Remember to use non-toxic glue.

3. Outline in black marker the shape of the puzzle pieces on a separate piece of paper or cardstock. This will serve as your template and guide your family member as to where the pieces go (see photo).

TIPS

- Provide verbal cues if needed.

- For your first puzzle, cut the photo into only two or three pieces. You can always make puzzles with more pieces at a later time.

- When making a face puzzle, include just the face. When there's too much going on in the background, it's distracting. Eliminate the clutter.

It's fun to do when the photo is of someone important to you or your family member.

ADAPTATIONS

More Challenging

- Increase the number of puzzle pieces.

- Cut out different shapes for the puzzle pieces. For example, instead of straight-edged pieces use curvy ones.

- Try the activity without the template.

Less Challenging

Look at the photos and reminisce.

- You do the puzzle with your family member watching.

- Create a two-piece puzzle to start with. Once your family member has mastered the two-piece puzzle, then you can try the same puzzle with three pieces and continue building in that manner.

- Put a number on the back of each puzzle piece. Put the corresponding number on the template where that piece should go.

- In a similar way, you can use color-coding to give cues to your family member.

- Instead of using only outlines of the puzzle pieces for a template, make a copy of the photo and use it as a template. Be sure to include the outline of the puzzle pieces.

- Just look at the photos and reminisce.

- Grandchildren can help with this activity.

Heritage Puzzle

DESCRIPTION

Our heritage gives us something to connect with on a grander, larger scale. Would you be interested in trying a unique puzzle with a cultural twist? Instead of putting pieces together that create a picture, this next activity consists of taking away pieces that reveal a picture underneath. The picture is of a flag or some other symbol or picture that represents you, your family member, and your roots. If you would like to give it a try, by all means, read on!

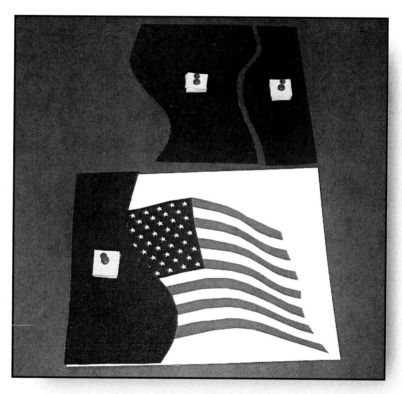

HOW TO

1. The first step to creating this activity is finding a picture of a flag that represents your heritage. (You can substitute a picture of something else that is meaningful to your family if you wish.) Be sure that it is a color picture and that it is large enough and clear enough to see. If you have access to the Internet and a color printer, you can look up clip art or images of flags and print one out. There are also flag calendars that you can purchase.

2. Once you have decided on a picture, your next step is to glue the picture to a background. The background should be a harder material to give some strength and durability to your picture. If your picture still bends easily after you have glued it onto your background, it is too flimsy. Cardstock or a piece of poster board would work well. If you want your background to be larger than the picture so it creates a border around the picture, then feel free to do that.

Try a unique puzzle with a cultural twist.

This may spark some wonderful memories.

3. Your next step is to create the pieces that will cover the picture of the flag. This is very simple. Take a piece of cardstock that is the same size as the background/picture combo. The goal here is for the cardstock to be large enough that when placed over the picture, complete with background, it covers the whole thing. Next, you just cut pieces out of the cardstock. Determine the number of pieces that you cut based on the abilities of your family member. You can always increase the difficulty level at a later time, so it is better to err on the side of caution and cut a smaller number of pieces to start out. If you are concerned that your family member may have difficulty gripping the pieces, you can attach pegs on the pieces for easier gripping. You can use your creativity here and make pegs as well.

4. Once you have cut out your "cover" pieces, put them together on top of the flag picture to be sure that they conceal the picture completely.

5. Present your unique puzzle to your family member. Demonstrate the idea of removing a piece at a time to uncover a surprise picture underneath. Once they have the idea, allow them to continue removing the pieces until the picture is revealed and a sign of their heritage appears before their eyes.

TIPS

• Allow reminiscence with this activity. If your family member starts uncovering the puzzle and enough of the picture is revealed for them to identify what it is, it may spark some wonderful memories. If this occurs and they start talking and stop uncovering, that is perfectly fine.

- If your family member has a difficult time manipulating the cardstock pieces, you can try craft foam to create them instead of cardstock. You can purchase craft foam at your local craft store. It is sold in single sheets or in packages.

- Typically, when pulling together an activity, we would encourage you to include your family member in the construction process. Because we want the picture underneath to be a mystery, you may want to be the sole creator this time.

- When you select a picture of a flag, try to choose one that features only the flag itself and not a lot of extras going on in the background. Extra background material distracts from the main focus of your picture.

ADAPTATIONS

More Challenging

- If you would like to make this activity more of a challenge, you can accomplish this in a few different ways. The simplest way is to make more pieces that need to be removed in order to uncover the picture.

- Also, you can add complexity through the cover pieces. Instead of using all one color, you can make cover pieces that are different colors. When it comes time to uncover the picture, you can tell your family member to remove "a red piece" or remove "a blue piece." This way, they are not only removing the pieces in attempts to discover the picture beneath, but they are color matching as well. You can also use different letters or numbers instead of colors. Write a different letter or number on every piece. Then, you could tell your family member to remove the "A" piece or the "Number 7 piece."

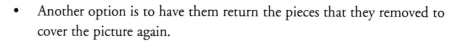

- Another option is to have them return the pieces that they removed to cover the picture again.

Just talk about the picture.

Less Challenging

- The simplest technique for decreasing the complexity level of this activity is to reduce the number of cover pieces that you use. You can use only one piece if you need to. If one proves to be too simple, change it to two or three pieces for the next time you try the activity.

- You can also reduce the workload on your family member, which would reduce the challenge. You can take turns with this activity. They remove one cover piece and then you remove one cover piece. This way you are cutting their work in half.

- Remove all the pieces in front of them as they watch, replace the pieces in the correct spot so the picture is hidden once again, and then have them try it.

- Or, you can remove all of the pieces yourself as they watch and just talk to them about the picture.

- And finally, you can change the level of complexity by removing the idea of uncovering a picture all together and simply show them a picture to reflect on and discuss.

Dominoes Revisited

DESCRIPTION

Do you love to play games? An old favorite is the game of Dominoes. It is probably a fan favorite because it can involve all ages and abilities. Young children can play along with a grandparent, making it a family affair. Maybe now is the time to dust off the family set and invite your loved one to play a game again.

HOW TO

1. There are two different sets of Dominoes. One set only includes numbers up to six. A second, more advanced set uses numbers up to 12. A suggestion would be to initially work with the first set.

2. Invite your loved one to join you at a table and begin by removing the domino tiles from the container. You can do this together. If this is a personal set, it may bring back many memories. Allow time to touch the tiles and remember.

3. Place all tiles face down on a tray. The tray can easily be moved to assist your loved one if they need the dominoes brought closer.

4. Each player chooses four tiles and places them in front of themselves. Usually, tiles are placed on their sides, but you can place the tiles face up in case your loved one needs assistance.

5. To begin the game, one person selects a tile from the tray and places it face up in the center between the players.

6. The next player sees if they have a tile with the same number and if so, places that tile next to its match, end to end (see photo).

7. If there is no match to play, you select one tile from the domino tray. If a match is drawn, then it can be played immediately.

8. The game continues until a player has no more tiles in front of them, until no more tiles can be played, or until everyone agrees to stop.

Dust off the family set and invite your loved one to play.

TIPS

- We suggest playing this game in a quiet place and sitting around a table.

- If your loved one has a vision impairment, you may want to locate a Dominoes set with larger tiles. Or, to save money, make your own set using white cardstock and a black marker to add the dots.

- A secret is to begin slowly. Just removing the tiles from the container might be the only step of this activity for the first couple of times. This slow process allows for increased engagement and may provide time to reminisce.

Put the well-worn rulebook aside.

- Another suggestion might be to put the well-worn rulebook aside. The new rule of thumb is to adapt, to anticipate, and to change the rules as you go. This will ensure fun and limit frustration. The goal is to have a good time together, not necessarily win or even finish the game.

- The game is over when one player begins to lose interest. It is always best to conclude before your loved one becomes tired.

ADAPTATIONS

More Challenging

- Increase the difficulty by using a set of tiles that has numbers up to 12.

- Combine two sets of Dominoes, each of which uses numbers up to six, so you have twice as many to work with.

Less Challenging

- Have a grandchild or someone assist your loved one in playing the game.

- Hand the domino to be played to your loved one and show them where to place it.

- Just watching a game being played might be fun for your loved one.

Target Practice

DESCRIPTION

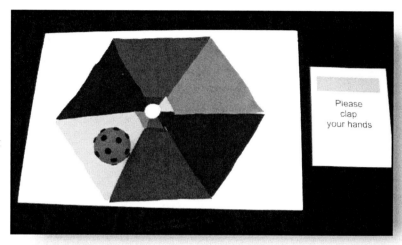

This is an activity reminiscent of the game of darts or archery and ideal for the sports-minded person. One of the great things about this game is that you have the power to construct the target! You decide the size, design, and colors to create a target just as your loved one would want it. Is there a particular target sport that your family member fondly recalls? If so, now is your chance to allow them to reconnect with those memories. If not, here's a chance for them to learn a new game.

HOW TO

1. The first step to this activity is gathering your supplies. You will need the following:

    a. **A Foam Board™.** This will serve as the backboard for your target. You can purchase Foam Board™ at craft stores.

    b. **Felt of various colors.** We would suggest a maximum of six different colors. The felt will be forming the different sections of your target. Felt is often available at craft stores, but if you cannot find it there, visit a fabric store.

    c. **Self-adhesive Velcro® dots.** These Velcro® dots can be purchased at craft stores as well. They will be adhered to the ball that will be thrown at the target.

Ideal for the sports-minded person

d.   **A ball.** When selecting your ball, look for something that is approximately the size of a large orange or a grapefruit, and made of some light material. If this is difficult to hold for your loved one, try a smaller ball. You may also want to bring some Velcro® dots with you when selecting the ball to ensure that the Velcro® adheres to the ball.

e.   **Non-toxic craft glue.** You will need glue to adhere the felt pieces to the backboard.

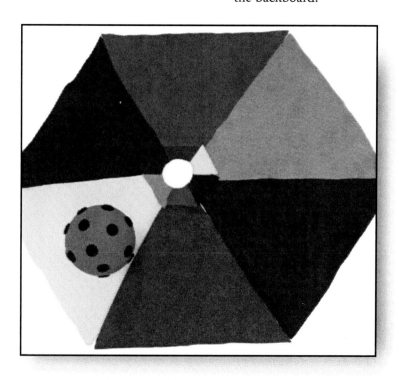

2.   Now that you have all of the necessary materials, your next step is to use them! To create your target, cut a pie-shaped section from each piece of felt. Make sure that all of the pie-shaped pieces are the same size. If you have six different colors of felt, then you should have six different colored pieces when you are finished.

3.   Glue the different pieces of felt to the Foam Board™, (see photo).

4.   If you would like, create a large bullseye for the center. Use your own creativity for a bullseye.

5.   Cover your ball with Velcro® dots.

6.   The next step is to make color-coordinated action cards that match the colors on the target. When we say "action cards," we mean cards that instruct you to do something. For example, if the ball is thrown and lands on the yellow section, you would select a yellow action card. The yellow card may read, "Sing a Song," "Raise Your Hands in the Air," "Clap Your Hands," "Stomp Your Feet," etc. You can write whatever you want on the action cards based on your family member's likes and abilities.

7. You are now ready to begin. Demonstrate for your family
    member by throwing the ball at the target.
    Whichever color it lands on, read the
    corresponding action card and do the
    requested action. Now turn the ball
    over to your family member and let
    them hit the target.

TIPS

- You can place the target on the
  floor and have your family
  member drop the ball on it or lean it
  up against something and have them
  throw the ball at the target.

- Move the target closer to anyone who can only drop or throw a short
  distance.

- Create the colored action cards with doable activities that your loved
  one can read and will enjoy.

- Feel free to change the rules as you go. Create an activity that works
  for your family member. What we present can serve as simply a
  starting point.

- The target can be any shape.

**Create an
activity
that works
for your
family
member.**

ADAPTATIONS

More Challenging

- Create a game with a competitive edge by numbering the different
  colored sections on your target and keeping score.

- Make action cards with more complex tasks on them. Instead of the action card saying "Tap your Head," it could say, "Tap your Head and Rub your Stomach."

- Have two targets and two teams for a competitive event.

- You could use blindfolds when throwing or dropping the ball.

- Using different-sized balls will increase the difficulty as well.

- Take pictures while doing the activity and make a scrapbook with your loved one to share with their friends. Remember to label all of the pictures using large print.

Have two targets and two teams for a competitive event.

Less Challenging

- You can throw the ball and your loved one can name the color where the ball hits the target.

- Your loved one can be the designated action card reader.

- You can have your family member simply observe others doing the activity. They are still participating through observation.

Rhythm Exercises

DESCRIPTION

When you listen to music that has a definite beat, do you find your fingers and toes keeping time? Many of us do. If you and your loved one fit this description, you will enjoy this activity. Playing an instrument or reading music is not required. This activity involves recorded music or simply turning on a favorite radio station. Once the music begins, enjoy listening to the music together while accompanying it using maracas or anything else. Create your own band!

HOW TO

Create your own band!

1. Maracas and rhythm instruments can be found, purchased, or made. For example, you can glue (non-toxic) two paper plates or bowls together with beans, rice, coins, etc. An empty orange juice can be turned into a rhythm instrument. Taping up the ends of an empty paper towel roll also works. We are not going to place any limits here!

2. All music is appropriate. You would definitely want to include your loved one's favorite tunes. If this is an unknown, you may wish to play a variety of different tunes and watch for positive responses and reminiscing. Remember, anything goes—orchestral pieces, big band selections, rock and roll, or Motown. You may not know what currently appeals to your loved one.

3. Choose a quiet, more private place to play your music so you do not hinder your loved one's creativity.

4. Play a short introduction to two selections and ask your loved one to choose which one they would enjoy.

5. While the music is being played, demonstrate shaking the maracas. Whenever you feel comfortable, invite your family member to join you by giving them a maraca to play. Now you're making music!

TIPS

- Different days may require different music. Some days you may need to be more upbeat and lively, while on others it might be better to use more calming tunes.

- If your loved one is hearing impaired, you may need to increase the volume. This is another reason for the more private space. You may also want to consider earphones; however, wearing earphones may be a new experience in itself.

- Revisiting this activity several times for short periods will make it more familiar.

ADAPTATIONS

More Challenging

Grandchildren of all ages can be very creative in forming a family band.

- Involve more of your family. Grandchildren of all ages can be very creative in forming a family band.

- If recorded music or a radio is not handy, hum or sing a song together while shaking the maracas.

- Create your own personalized maracas. The sky is the limit! Have your family member help decorate their maracas.

- Another activity is to copy rhythmic patterns. You shake your maracas three times and ask your family member to copy you. You can then switch roles and your loved one plays a rhythm for you to imitate. Again, this activity can involve all ages. Children especially love to improvise and create their own rhythms.

Less Challenging

- Introduce the maracas or any rhythm instrument without background music. This allows time to manipulate the instrument and become more comfortable shaking it.

- You can assist your loved one by holding their hands and helping them shake the maracas. Just be sure that doing so won't cause them pain or make them anxious.

- Simply listen to the music. Or, they can just observe others engaged in this fun-filled activity. Your loved one is still involved while watching and listening.

- Clapping, tapping the table with your hands, or tapping your feet are also great ways to improvise.

Sing-a-Long

DESCRIPTION

You do not need a special talent to participate in this next activity. All you need is a desire to have some fun! This wonderful activity incorporates all ages and all levels of ability. You pair up with your loved one, or even your whole family, and join together in song. Once singing begins, words from these familiar tunes come streaming back.

HOW TO

To do this activity, you just need to choose an approach. There are a few different options. You can present the following choices to your loved one and see what type of response you get. If they are having difficulty choosing, you make the selection. Here are some ways it can be done:

1. Simply turn on a favorite recording, preferably the oldies, and listen to the selections. Whenever you hear that old time favorite that your family member loves, burst into song. This will hopefully influence your loved one to follow suit. If not, keep singing. They may join in later.

2. Another approach is to create your own songbook of family favorites. You may want to try some patriotic, religious, or popular show tunes—whatever you think will appeal to your family member.

3. How about that old record player and the prized collection of albums in storage? These albums undoubtedly hold many great memories. You can plan a revival. Besides old memories for your loved one, this antique may just be the thing for a history lesson for the grandchildren. Put on the albums and sing along.

Create your own songbook of family favorites.

TIPS

• If creating a songbook is not convenient for you, you can always purchase a songbook of familiar selections.

• Choose a quiet space to sit together. This shared time will give your loved one that special individual attention and also enable all participants to hear.

• Make sure that the printing in the songbooks is large enough for your family member to read.

- People often remember only a couple of lines of a popular hit, such as the chorus. If this is the case, sing just the chorus. You can repeat this as many times as you wish. For another approach, you sing the verses and they sing the chorus (with you, if necessary). Who said that you need to know the whole song?

- Family gatherings are wonderful opportunities to start a new tradition: family sing-a-longs. Gathering around a piano or someone playing a guitar can create wonderful family memories.

ADAPTATIONS

More Challenging

Have your loved one help to create a songbook.

- Have your loved one help to create a songbook. Allow them, if possible, to choose the songs that they enjoy most and decide which to include in their songbook. They can listen to records, tapes, CDs, or the radio or choose selections from a written list of favorites.

- A new twist might be to have your loved one help to create invitations requesting friends to join in a fun-filled night of singing.

- An all-time favorite is a talent show. Young children may love an opportunity to perform for the family and are especially fun to watch. You can have your family member help to put on a family talent show. Someone is the designated M.C., and family members, including the grandchildren, are the performers.

- Karaoke machines are readily available to rent and are great fun for all ages. Rent a machine, unless you already have one, and sing along with your loved ones.

- Singing can also involve costumes and dance. White gloves and hats can be worn during a performance. Tambourines or paper plates can be moved or shaken in time to the beat.

Less Challenging

- Participation might simply be observing others singing and enjoying the group dynamics.

- Instead of choosing the selections or assembling the songbook, possibly your family member can help to decorate the cover of the songbook. Their creativity is definitely encouraged and welcomed. This can be done as a group project or as an individual project.

- Ask your loved one to select the next song or give them a choice of two selections. If necessary, they can simply point to the choice.

Musical Hands

DESCRIPTION

The musical hands activity is simply fun! If your loved one enjoys music or was a musician or dancer, this activity is not only enjoyable, but shares a special significance because it takes them back to their glory days. Another great aspect of this activity is that it is perfect to do together as a family or with a group of residents. Music is played on a CD, tape or record player. Everyone in the group claps to the music, but the music will be stopped at random points by the person leading the activity. When the music stops, the group needs to stop clapping.

HOW TO

1. Another great benefit to an activity such as this one is that there is nothing to make. All that you need is to have access to a CD, tape or record player, and some chairs.

2. Set the chairs up in a circle with your chair positioned next to the source of music. That's it!

TIPS

This is perfect to do together as a family or with a group of residents.

- Be sure to set the chairs up in a circle. When the chairs are in a circle, your field of vision includes all participants in the group. This will help to keep everyone focused on the activity.

- Choose music that your family member and other older adults would enjoy. An older adult may not appreciate pop, rock, or heavy metal! Also, if at all possible, use recorded music instead of the radio. This way, advertisements, traffic and weather reports, etc., will not continue to interrupt your game.

- A very important tip to keep in mind is the following: because there is no losing in a Montessori-Based activity, we do not want to promote the idea of winners and losers. The idea is just to have fun, so do not eliminate people who get caught clapping after the music has stopped. Encourage the participants in the group to continue clapping and you focus on keeping the laughs rolling!

- Children can be brought into the activity, and their enthusiasm can liven up your family member's day.

A great activity for people who may not be able to express themselves verbally

• Do not limit this activity to simply hand clapping. If you are doing this activity in a nursing home, some residents may not be able to clap their hands. They can, however, possibly tap their feet or bob their head. Whatever they can do, invite them to participate. This activity can serve as a great socializing activity for people who may not be able to express themselves verbally. This places the focus on what can be done, which is exactly the goal of this whole Montessori-Based approach.

ADAPTATIONS

More Challenging

• To make this activity more challenging, you can stop the music more frequently and after shorter intervals of time. For example, you can play it for a 30-40 second span before stopping it, but then play it again for only 10 seconds. This helps the participants stay engaged.

• Continually changing the stopping pattern can increase the challenge as well. When you keep changing the pattern, the participants cannot figure out your method and will continue to be surprised. Also, you can increase the challenge by turning your back to the group so they cannot see when you reach over to stop the music. This way they have to pay very close attention because they no longer have the visual cue of when you are going to make the stop.

Less Challenging

• To reduce the challenge of this activity, you can keep the same stopping pattern every time. For example, you can stop the music every 30 seconds or stop the music every minute. This gives the participants the opportunity to learn your procedure.

• You can also reduce the challenge by saying, "stop!" when you stop the music. This serves as an additional, fairly blatant cue.

• Also, you can eliminate the whole idea of stopping the clapping when the music stops. Just have your group clap their hands to the music. This is still a very engaging activity, but eliminates that extra challenge of the stopping.

• If your family member has difficulty clapping, but can wave an arm, have them hold a paper plate and wave it back and forth when the music plays. The paper plate can reflect different times of the year or special occasions, such as birthdays, the Fourth of July, etc.

• And finally, if your family member or a resident in the group is experiencing difficulty with this activity, you can have them be the designated music stopper. You can show them the button to press and sit beside them to assist, but allow them to be in the driver's seat.

Playing an Instrument

DESCRIPTION

Many people have been gifted with the unique ability to make music. For those who enjoyed playing an instrument, music brings back fond memories. This activity introduces a new approach—no practicing necessary!

HOW TO

1. Do you have a picture or a tape of your loved one playing a musical instrument? Sharing this would be a great first step toward reminding them of this old, but new activity.

2. A second step may be to play a favorite piece of recorded instrumental music. Start to get them back into that musical groove!

3. And how about that old instrument? If you still have it stashed away somewhere, dig it out! We are not suggesting that you spend money reconditioning or tuning the instrument, or even that your family member will pick up playing where they left off. But you may want to encourage some holding and feeling time. Let them get reacquainted with their old friend. Reminiscing is an important time, especially when it has to do with an old hobby that can be reintroduced in some capacity.

4. Ask if they would like to play, and assist them as needed.

TIPS

- Timing of this activity is especially important because interruptions and distractions decrease focus.

- Keep in mind the old adage, "Short and Sweet!" You want to be sure to conclude on a positive "note" after a few minutes, unless more time is requested.

ADAPTATIONS

More Challenging

- A more challenging activity might be a matching and sorting activity with pictures. You would have pictures of instruments and labels with the instruments' names. The object would be to match the pictures with the corresponding labels. You would want to label the back of each picture with the correct instrument name to serve as an additional cue if needed.

If you still have that old instrument, dig it out!

- Another adaptation could be to look at music magazines together, pick out different instruments, and talk about how they have changed over the years.

- You could also create a tape playing different instruments and ask your loved one to identify the instrument being played. You could place cards in front of them with each card picturing one of the instruments on the tape as well as the word identifying the instrument. They could point to the instrument's card when they think that they are hearing the corresponding sounds on the tape. Remember, the goal is to enjoy this activity! Give all the cues necessary to help them complete it while feeling good about themselves at the same time.

Less Challenging

- If you do not have an instrument to bring out or you think that this activity is a little too complex, you can introduce music in a different way. You might want to provide some recordings of their favorite tunes and performers to be played throughout the day. How great would it be to have something available to play during stressful times, during morning routines, exercise times, at night if unable to sleep, etc.?

Arrange for a special concert by a "budding soloist."

- If your family member did play an instrument, but may have difficulty using the instrument now, you can do something less complex. Hang up a picture of the instrument that your loved one played. Or, you can hang up a picture of your loved one playing their instrument. If your family member lives in a facility, this will enable caregivers to know more about your loved one and create more meaningful conversations. If they live at home, it can serve as a reminder. Perhaps you should also enlarge the picture so they could see it easier.

- Schedule a special movie time—begin by renting a videotape or DVD of an orchestral performance. At holiday times, there are many selections. Watch it together. It may be a good idea to divide this viewing over several periods.

- Finally, you may wish to schedule a visit incorporating a private concert given by a grandchild or friend. Another idea would be to contact a local high school to arrange for a special concert by a "budding soloist." The wonderful aspect of this activity validates the student and provides pleasure to the listening audience.

Bean Bag Toss

DESCRIPTION

Here is a great activity for all ages and abilities. Bean bags can be dropped, tossed, or thrown. They can be different sizes, textures, and weights. Let's create an activity designed specifically for your loved one.

HOW TO

1. Bean bags can be purchased or handmade.
   If you would like to purchase them, they are often found at toy stores or possibly sports stores. They can also be bought over the Internet. A quick way to make a bean bag is to put dried beans in a sock and tie off the end.

2. Choose the bean bag game that you think would be appropriate for your family member. There are several game options that can be played from a sitting or standing position. Here are some suggestions:

   a. The bean bags can be dropped into a basket that is placed on the floor or on a chair.

   b. Place squares of different-colored construction paper on the floor. Match the colors of the construction paper to the colors of the bean bags. Throw or drop the bean bags onto the matching colored square.

   c. The bean bags can also be thrown to another person for a game of catch.

   d. Another tossing alternative is to throw the bean bags through a plastic hoop, which someone holds up. The person can easily move the plastic hoop around.

This is a great activity for all ages!

TIPS

- You can make or purchase as many bean bags as you wish and keep them in a special basket. Grandchildren will remember this basket and look forward to playing this activity with your loved one. They can even play with the bean bags by themselves during a visit.

- Specific textures and colors may have special appeal. If your loved one likes the color red, you can make all red bean bags in different textures such as velvet, corduroy, silk, fake fur, and cotton. You can also create a variety by doing different patterns all in red.

- Another suggestion might be to make two of each kind of bean bag.

ADAPTATIONS

More Challenging

- If you are making your own bean bags, have your loved one assist.

- Place pieces of different-colored construction paper on the floor. Assign point values to colors to keep score. For example, yellow equals five points, red equals one, etc.

- If you are keeping score as mentioned above, you can create a game, such as a horse race. For example, if you have two players, each can be assigned a horse or a marker. Each horse or marker would be moved on a game board by the number of spaces that corresponds with the score from a tossed bean bag. After moving a certain number of spaces, the horse would cross a "finish line."

- Increase the level of difficulty by moving the basket, plastic hoop, or colored paper further away to challenge them.

Less Challenging

- If baskets are used, feel free to have someone pick up the basket to try to help catch the tossed bean bags.

- Papers, baskets, or hoops can be moved closer.

- Have your loved one sort the different bean bags according to color, pattern, texture and/or weight.

- Have your loved one be the official bean bag holder and you or other family members can be the throwers.

Centerpiece Construction

DESCRIPTION

The table centerpiece activity allows your family member to feel creative and proud over and over again. This activity consists of creating an attractive centerpiece for display in your family member's home. Whether home is an apartment, house, or nursing home, it is nice to give it a personal touch. A vase, colored marbles, and fruits, vegetables, feathers, or flowers are compiled into an arrangement that will remind your loved one of their many talents.

HOW TO

1. Decide what type of arrangement you are going to make. Ask your family member, but give them a few options to choose from. Our suggestions: peacock feathers, plastic fruits and vegetables with stems, greenery, or flowers. We would only suggest using the vegetables and fruits with someone who would not think they are real and attempt to eat them. If you think that this is a possibility, go with one of the other choices.

2. Once you and your family member have made a decision, go shopping for your supplies. You can buy your materials at any local craft store. Even dollar stores have a lot of these types of materials.

   a. You will need a vase. If you are interested in using a glass vase, and your loved one lives in any type of facility, ask permission to use glass first. You can also use a plastic vase. Regardless of what kind you choose, try to make it a smaller vase to keep the scale of the project reasonable.

   b. You will need something to hold your arrangement in place. We suggest choosing colored marbles or stones to go in the bottom of the vase. It would probably be best if the stones were not clear or white. These colors may be more difficult to see. If your family member can help choose the marbles or stones, that's a bonus!

Family members feel creative and proud over and over again.

c. The next step is choosing the items that will make up the arrangement. We would suggest getting about eight items, but not necessarily using all eight. It is always good to have a few extra materials available in case you want to practice before constructing the final product.

d. You will also need a container or a plastic bowl to place your marbles or stones in.

3. You are now ready to begin setting up. To prepare for the first step, you should pour the marbles into a plastic container or dish. Place the container or dish of marbles on the left and the vase on the right since your family member will be working from left to right.

It is always good to have a few extra materials available.

4. There are really only a couple of steps to this activity, but you should still have your family member do only one step at a time. The first step is to fill the bottom of the vase with the colored marbles. Before asking your family member to start filling the vase, be sure to demonstrate first. It is probably not necessary to use your full bowl of marbles, but there needs to be enough marbles to hold your feathers or fruits, or whatever material you use, securely in place. Allow your family member to use as many marbles as they want, but if it seems to be too little, you could encourage them to add a few more.

5. Once they have filled the bottom of the vase with marbles, it's time to work with the feathers, greenery, fruits, flowers, etc. in front of them. Once again, demonstrate the next step. It is particularly important to demonstrate here because you need them to push the feather (for example) down into the marbles to secure it in the vase. Once you have demonstrated, allow them to choose where the feathers go, unless they ask you for some assistance. This is their arrangement, so we need to refrain from dictating too much where things go unless they need the instruction.

6. The next step to this activity is something for you to do, with your family member's help if possible. Your job is to make sure that your loved one continues to experience that proud feeling of creating their centerpiece. To ensure this, we suggest creating a tag to put in the centerpiece that says "Made together by _____ and her daughter, _____(or her son, or grandson, etc.). You and your family member can also compose your own message for the tag. Your family member might help by lettering the tag. Make sure that your tag is clearly visible (large, dark writing on a light background) and you can attach it to a rod of some kind (possibly a wooden rod or chopstick). This way, your family member will have bragging rights to that centerpiece for months to come!

7. Finally, display the centerpiece. How wonderful if your family member lives in a nursing home to have their centerpiece prominently displayed on their table in the dining room! Everyone at that table and all walking by will be able to see the work of your family member. Note: If your loved one lives in any type of facility, seek permission first, of course.

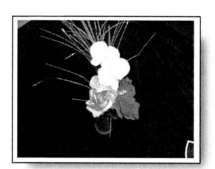

TIPS

- Be aware! You are working with some potentially problematic materials here: colored marbles, possibly glass, and artificial fruits and vegetables. If you think that a glass vase is not a good idea, or your family member may put either the marbles or the fruits or vegetables in their mouth, do not use these materials. You can use plastic vases or baskets for the centerpiece. Use colored sand at the bottom of the vase instead of marbles. (Use a funnel when pouring the sand into the vase.) You can also choose peacock feathers or greenery or flowers instead of the fruits or vegetables. You can also choose your own material to make the centerpiece. Our suggestions are just to give you ideas. You can choose anything you think would work well and that your family member would enjoy.

- Make sure that nothing sharp is at the bottom of the items that you chose for your arrangement. In other words, make sure that there is no floral wiring hanging out, etc. If there is, you need to fix that or use something else.

ADAPTATIONS

More Challenging

- Make your arrangement larger. Use a bigger vase and more materials. Remember, if at first you are not confident that your family member can work with a larger arrangement, build up to it instead.

- You can also increase the challenge by having them create additional centerpieces that they can give as gifts. This way, your loved one also experiences the joy of giving to someone else.

Less Challenging

- Go smaller. You can get a single bud vase and use only one feather or flower or whatever material you choose.

- You can do the actual construction of the arrangement and your family member can hand you the feathers or greenery.

- Your family member can watch while you physically construct the arrangement. Ask them their opinion at every step. "Do you think that this feather looks good here?" "Do you like this flower or this one?"

- Find a bridal or decorating magazine and look at centerpieces or bouquets together.

Reach for the Color

DESCRIPTION

This is an activity that will encourage your family member to reach and stretch. You can practice working on range of motion by having your loved one reach for different colors.

HOW TO

1. Make or find a small cube-shaped box. Color each side with markers (non-toxic) so that each side will be a different color.

2. Using the template we provide after this activity description, draw six circles on paper. Color the circles the same colors as the sides of the box (see photo).

3. Place the circles on a table in front of your family member.

4. You are ready to begin! One player rolls the box. Whichever color is on the top of the box, the other player will place their hand on the corresponding colored circle.

5. The game proceeds by each player taking turns rolling the box or touching a circle.

Encourage your family member to reach and stretch.

TIPS

- You can purchase a pre-made cube box at your local craft store.

- This can be a good intergenerational activity to help include younger children.

ADAPTATIONS

More Challenging

- Have your family member help create the circles and box.

- Try this activity by placing the circles on the floor and touching them with your feet.

- The game can be more challenging when colored circles are placed around the room. When a color is rolled, move to that circle.

Less Challenging

- Use fewer circles and fewer colors on the box.

- Have your family member call out the color that was rolled.

- If your family member has trouble rolling the box, they can just drop it on the floor.

- Instead of taking turns, team up your family member with another player, such as a grandchild.

Have your family member help create the circles and box.

COLOR TEMPLATE

Cut out the template and make copies to color. Your loved one can help!

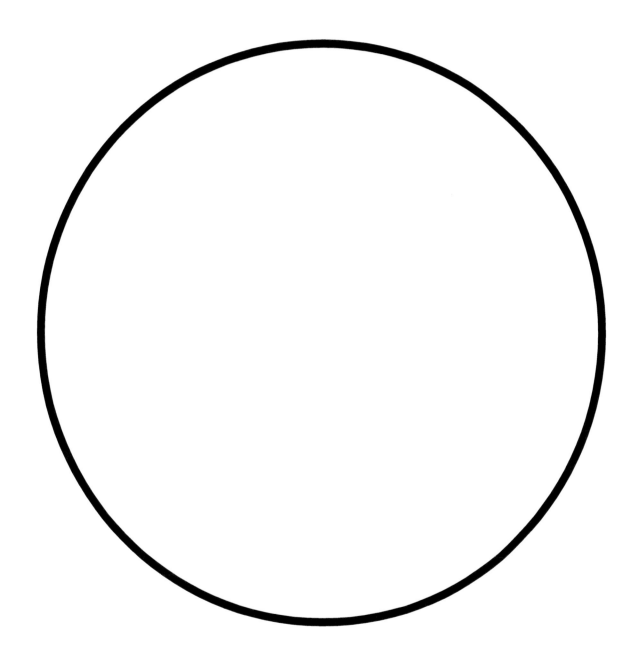

Nuts & Bolts

DESCRIPTION

This activity may bring out the carpenter in your family member. The idea is to screw together nuts with their corresponding bolts. Because you are using real nuts and bolts, this activity not only stimulates the mind, but also requires your family member to exercise those hands!

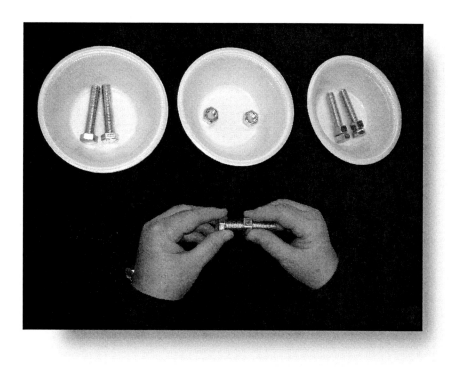

HOW TO

1. To make this activity, you will need five large nuts and bolts of the same size (see photo).

2. To do this activity, you will need three bowls, all set up in a row. The first bowl will be for the bolts. The second bowl will be for the nuts. The third bowl will be the "finished" bowl, where your family member places the nut-bolt combination after they have screwed them together.

3. To begin, as always, you demonstrate. The idea is to pick up a bolt from the first container and a nut from the second container and screw them together. Once they are screwed together, you place them in the third "finished" container. Every bolt and nut that they attempt to match should fit together properly because they are all the same size. You have the opportunity to increase the challenge of this activity at a later time, but as we always suggest, start off simple!

4. Continue in this manner until all five sets are matched up.

This stimulates the mind, and exercises those hands!

TIPS

- Be aware! Even though you are using the large size bolts and nuts, you are still working with fairly small objects. If you think that there is a possibility of your family member placing these objects in their mouth, you should choose a different activity.

- Make sure that the nuts and bolts fit together easily before giving them to your family member to work with.

ADAPTATIONS

More Challenging

- To increase the difficulty of this activity, you can present matching nuts and bolts of different sizes. Choose small, medium, and large sets.

- To increase the challenge further, use a wide variety of matching nuts and bolts of different sizes.

- Turn the activity into a category sort and add additional categories. For example, you can add screws and anchors to the mix. You would have a bowl of nuts, bolts, screws, and anchors and the object would be to divide them all up into their corresponding categories.

- Another adaptation is to buy small brackets that the nuts and bolts could be used to assemble. The goal of this activity would then become one of assembling the brackets (see photo).

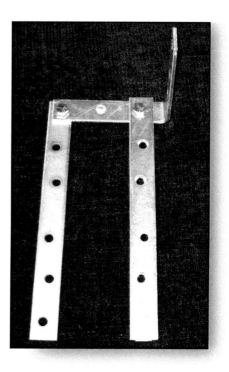

Less Challenging

- Ask your family member simply to sort between the nuts and the bolts. You would still use three containers: one for the nuts and bolts combined, one to place the nuts into, and one for the bolts.

- Have your family member count the nuts or bolts or both.

Guessing Bags

DESCRIPTION

Guessing Bags are great for individuals who have visual, memory, or hearing deficits. This activity involves identifying objects hidden within bags. The magic of this activity is that it relies on the sense of touch.

HOW TO

1. The first step is to choose a target object. You will place the target object in front of your family member, and they will attempt to locate its match within the Guessing Bags. This object can be anything, as long as it is familiar, not dangerous, and you have two of them that are exactly the same. For example, you could use silk flowers or plastic spoons.

2. Once you have selected your target object, then you can choose the other objects to place in the bags. We suggest a target object and two others to begin with. Be sure to choose objects that are clearly distinguishable from the target object to make the match easier. For example, if you chose a spoon as your target object, then the objects inside the bags could be a brush, a pencil, and a matching spoon.

3. Next, select your bags. Cloth or burlap bags work best. In a pinch, socks can be used. Keep in mind when selecting your bags that you will need to be able to fit your hand inside.

4. Finally, place your objects in the bags. Put only one object in each bag. Place the target object directly in front of your family member.

5. Reach into one of the bags and feel the object inside. Point to the target and say, "I don't think these are the same." Invite your family member to reach into the remaining bags until they find a match with the target.

The magic of this activity is that it relies on the sense of touch.

TIPS

- Make the objects as different from each other as possible.

- Assist when needed or asked.

ADAPTATIONS

More Challenging

- Add more bags.

- Use two bags, with each bag holding the same three objects. The goal is now to match up the pairs of objects between the two bags.

- Place pairs of objects in the same bag, and have your family member match up the pairs.

- Take matching out of the activity. Instead, try to have your family member identify the objects in each bag simply by touch. You may want to have a list of the objects that are in the bags placed in front of your family member to help them.

Less Challenging

- Use only two bags so the choice for the match is between only two, clearly different objects.

- Allow your family member to look in the bags to find the match, or use clear plastic bags. Even without guessing, you still have manipulation of materials, cognitive stimulation, and emotional bonding, all of which are very significant.

The goal is to match up pairs of objects.

Hand Massage

DESCRIPTION

Many women and men love the idea of being pampered. An easy way to do this is through a hand massage. When this experience is shared with a loved one, it is a wonderful indulgence.

HOW TO

1. Before doing this activity, take into consideration conditions such as arthritis or sensitive skin. Please consult your family physician on these matters.

2. Ideally, this experience is enhanced by creating a spa-like environment. Select a quiet place, dim the lights, and play a relaxing recording. You are ready to begin!

3. Next, choose a comfortable chair with a back support for your family member. A small pillow placed at the back of the chair may make it more comfortable to lean back and relax. Your loved one's wheelchair can also be adapted for additional support and comfort.

4. The second step is to offer your family member a choice of two or three different lotions. If your loved one has a favorite fragrance, you might wish to include that as a choice.

5. Sit comfortably in front of your loved one and begin by gently placing one of their hands in your hands. Time and touch communicate so much to your loved one.

6. Apply a small amount of lotion. Slowly, and with a very gentle touch, begin to massage each finger and then the hand. The key words here are "slowly and gently." The goal of this activity is relaxation.

Everyone loves to be pampered.

TIPS

Set aside the time you need for this activity.

- A key point is to set aside the time you need for this activity.

- There is no time limit. You might take 15 minutes or longer. But it's really up to you and your family member.

- Encourage your loved one to take a few deep breaths and close their eyes when you start the massage.

- This activity may be either non-verbal or a time to reminisce. You and your loved one decide.

- You may want to enhance the mood by introducing aromas, such as lavender.

- Do not rush! You have set aside this time, so enjoy.

ADAPTATIONS

More Challenging

- For the next spa treatment, you may wish to extend this activity to incorporate a neck and shoulder massage.

- Don't forget the feet! Some people, believe it or not, love to have foot massages!

- If your family member is able, you can also increase the complexity of this activity by having them massage your hands. How special that might be!

Less Challenging

- Holding hands during a visit may be just what your loved one needs. Touch is an important way to stay connected, especially for those that do not communicate verbally.

- Let your loved one smell the different scented lotions.

Pearls of Wisdom

DESCRIPTION

We live and we learn, as the saying goes. With older age comes greater knowledge. Would you be interested in doing an activity that captures some of your loved one's wisdom? If so, this next activity may be the right one for you. This is a sensory activity and can be used with many different people. Simply using the sense of touch can complete it. The object of this activity is to locate hidden "pearls of wisdom."

HOW TO

1. The first step to create this activity is to gather your supplies. You will need the following materials:

   a. A clear plastic bowl or container. A medium-sized bowl would be sufficient.

   b. Pearls (fake, of course!). You can purchase bags of pearl beads at your local craft store. There are bags of all white pearls and bags of colored-pearl mixtures. Choose whichever you prefer. You need enough pearls to cover about one third of your bowl. If the price of these pearl beads is too high, you can replace them with plain white round beads to get the same effect or mix in white beads with the pearls.

   c. Empty film canisters. The film canisters will be hidden inside the bowl of pearls, and each one will hold a "pearl of wisdom" saying. If you do not have film canisters, you can use something else to hold the sayings in, but it has to be something that your loved one can easily find when searching through the pearl beads.

We live and we learn.

2. The second step is the fun part! Think of the sayings that you want to include. Throughout your lifetime, you have probably heard countless quips, sayings, and advice from your family member. For example, did your loved one tell you after you suffered a broken heart that "time mends all wounds," or "time wounds all heels?" Or, if something didn't happen as you wanted it to, that "everything happens for a reason?" If so, these are the types of sayings that you could include in this activity. Think of five sayings that your loved one was known for using in their past or still uses today.

3. Write or type each saying on a piece of paper in dark marker or ink. Cut out each saying on a separate strip of paper. Fold each piece of paper up and place each one in its own film canister. Hide the film canisters in the bowl full of pearls.

4. You are ready to begin. The object is to reach in the bowl, sift through the pearls, and find a hidden canister which contains a pearl of wisdom saying. After each hidden "pearl" is found, you can either read it right then; or, hold all of the pearls until the end, open the canisters, and read them all at once. Demonstrate this process for your loved one and then have them continue to find the remaining pearls.

TIPS

With older age comes greater knowledge.

- If the price of pearl or regular beads is too high, you can substitute either of these with uncooked rice or popcorn kernels. The pearls and/or beads were just to look pretty and go along with the theme! Rice and kernels serve the same purpose.

- If you don't have film canisters, you can substitute small plastic eggs or small ring boxes.

- Be careful while doing this activity. You are working with small objects, whether they are beads, rice, or popcorn kernels. If there is a chance that your loved one would place any of these items in their mouth, choose a different activity.

ADAPTATIONS

More Challenging

- Use a larger bowl or fewer canisters, which would make more area to sift through to find the hidden treasures!

- Do not put the sayings inside of canisters. Just fold or roll the sayings up and hide them in the pearls.

- Compile a book of your favorite "pearls of wisdom" together.

- To make a very challenging but fun activity, hide one saying (written in large print on a full-sized piece of paper) in a room in your loved one's home. Have your loved one join forces with their grandchildren to locate the saying that is hidden in the room. You can give hints ("hot" or "cold") about whether they're close to the "pearl of wisdom" or not.

Less Challenging

- Use more canisters or a smaller bowl. This makes it easier to find "pearls."

- Do not entirely conceal the canisters in the bowl of pearls. Have the tops peaking out so your family member has a visual cue as to where they are.

- Eliminate the idea of hiding the canisters in the pearls. Place the canisters in the glass bowl without the pearls. The object would be to take them out and just read them. If needed, you can take the sayings out of the canisters and just put them in the glass bowl by themselves.

- Eliminate the idea of finding hidden sayings in a bowl of pearls. Instead, sit together and read a book of sayings.

- Do the activity as originally described, but have a grandchild help. This way, your loved one is sharing their knowledge with another generation.

Compile a book of your favorite "pearls of wisdom" together.

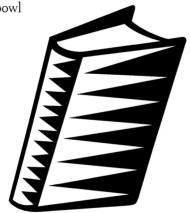

Taste Testing

DESCRIPTION

This activity puts those taste buds to work! Whether you enjoyed cooking or just enjoyed eating what was cooked, sampling the food was always a part of the fun. Why not make an activity out of it? This project does just that by creating an activity out of tasting some foods and guessing what they are.

HOW TO

Put those taste buds to work.

1. Sanitize your hands, those of your family member, and the utensils you will be using before beginning. You are going to be handling food samples, so cleanliness is a must!

2. Select three different foods that you think your loved one would recognize and enjoy. (Be sure it's alright for them to eat these foods first.) You can use three fruits such as a banana, peach, and a strawberry. If your family member loves candies, you can choose a chocolate bar, peanut butter candy, and licorice, etc.

3. After you have selected your foods, cut or break each one into five bite-sized pieces and place the pieces in three separate containers, one for each food.

4. Make labels for the foods and place the labels in front of your family member to guide them in identifying the foods when they taste them.

5. You are ready to begin. Demonstrate by picking up a piece of the food with the appropriate utensil, closing your eyes, putting the food into your mouth, and then pointing to the label that matches the food you just tasted.

6. Continue the taste match with your family member by asking them to close their eyes, placing samples into their mouth with the appropriate utensil and asking them to point to the labels that match.

Add more foods to classify.

7. Have fun sampling and conclude the activity whenever you want.

TIPS

- Do not forget about special dietary restrictions. If you are doing this activity with a family member, you are probably very familiar with their dietary restrictions. However, if you are doing this with a client or a resident in a facility, etc., find out if this activity is appropriate before you proceed. We would not recommend this activity for people with food allergies, special diets, or who have trouble swallowing.

ADAPTATIONS

More Challenging

- Add more foods to classify. Instead of starting out with three different foods, start out with four or five.

- Use the foods to create a snack together. If your three foods were bananas, strawberries, and peaches, make a fruit salad after tasting them.

- Try to select from three different but similar beverages, such as three kinds of cola, three fruit drinks, or three different wines.

- Have a wine and cheese tasting party.

Less Challenging

- Use three foods that are very different in taste and texture, like celery, a potato chip, and a chocolate chip.

- Let your family member eat with their hands instead of a utensil.

- Instead of taste matching, just put three foods in a basket and create accompanying labels for the foods. Put the labels in front of your family member and have them take the foods out of the basket and place them with their appropriate label.

- Another option is to remove the labels. Place two of each food in a basket and have your family member match up the pairs.

- Have your family member simply taste different foods without asking them to match anything. As it stated in the description of this activity, "sampling the food was always a part of the fun!" In this case, the sampling of the food would be the entire activity instead of a part of it.

Cook your family member's favorite recipe while they watch.

- Cook your family member's favorite recipe while they watch and just enjoy their favorite meal together.

Prayer Activity

DESCRIPTION

This can be used for individuals who cannot attend religious services as much as they would like. The Prayer Activity brings a component of religion to the individual. A

prayer is divided into its individual lines, and then the lines are mixed up. The object of the activity is to put the lines of the prayer in the correct order.

HOW TO

1. The first step is to pick out an appropriate prayer. Choose a prayer that holds a special significance for your family member.

2. Once you have selected the prayer, type it on a computer. Use your own judgment as to the number of words per line. Type in large (at least 48 pt.), Arial font. If you do not have access to a computer, print it on a piece of paper in black marker. Make sure that your writing is large and legible.

3. Once the prayer is typed or written in lines, cut each line into a single strip. Be sure to keep a separate, complete copy of the prayer.

Great for individuals who cannot attend religious services

TIPS

- To provide cues to the completion of this activity, number the back of each strip. Make sure that the numbers on the back match the line number in the prayer. For example, Line #1 of the prayer, should be labeled #1 on the back of the strip as well. Line #2 of the prayer should be labeled #2 on the back, etc.

- For further cueing, you can put a colored circle on the back of each strip. Make sure each strip has a circle of a different color. Next, make a template by taking a piece of white construction paper and outlining each strip on the paper, forming a single column (see photo). The strip outlines on the construction paper should match the colors of the circles on the backs of the prayer strips. For example, if the first line of the prayer has a red circle on its back, the first outline on the construction paper would be red as well. If Line #2 has a blue circle on its back, the second outline on the construction paper would also be blue, etc.

ADAPTATIONS

Share this activity with a child or friend.

More Challenging

- To make this activity more challenging, you can choose a longer prayer.

- Or, you can eliminate the use of any cues.

- You could ask your family member to help create the materials for the activity.

- Your family member could also share this activity with a child or a friend.

- Most challenging of all, you could ask your family member to come up with their own prayer, such as a prayer for peace.

Less Challenging

- Provide your family member with a complete copy of the prayer to help in putting the prayer strips in order. While less challenging, there is still a great deal going on within this activity, such as manipulation of materials as well as matching and cognitive stimulation.

Judging Length

DESCRIPTION

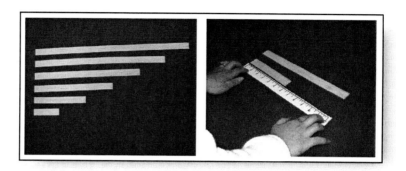

This activity stimulates the mind and works the hands. The object is to judge length by placing strips of balsa wood in order from longest to shortest. Many occupations, such as carpentry, design, and home repair, rely on the ability to accurately measure and judge length. Let's sharpen those skills!

HOW TO

1. This type of activity is a fan favorite because it does not require much construction. Purchase two 3-inch by 36-inch strips of balsa wood at your local craft store. Measure and cut each strip into 1-inch by 36-inch pieces. You will end up with six yardstick-sized strips.

2. Use these strips to make six pieces, each of a different length: 6-inches, 12-inches, 18-inches, 24-inches, 30-inches, and 36-inches (see photo). You will have leftovers for any adaptations.

3. Once you have all of your pieces cut, you are ready to begin. Put all of the pieces of balsa wood in front of your family member in a random order.

4. Do a demonstration for your family member. Take the longest strip of balsa wood in the group and place it first. Find the second longest piece of wood and place it below the first. Next, invite your family member to continue ordering the pieces from longest to shortest.

5. Once your family member has graded the strips in order, you can have them help you put the pieces away. You can ask them to hand you the longest strip followed by the shortest, etc.

TIPS

- Balsa wood can be cut with scissors.

A favorite because it does not require much construction

- If you do not think that grading strips of balsa wood would interest your family member, substitute these strips with something else. For example, if your loved one was a seamstress, they may be more interested in grading pieces of ribbon. You could also use craft foam or poster board—whatever is available.

- Remember, preparing materials together for an activity is a great activity in and of itself!

ADAPTATIONS

More Challenging

Ask for suggestions from your loved one as you grade the strips.

- Have your family member do the grading of the strips as instructed above. Once they have finished, you can mix the strips up and have your family member grade them again, but this time from shortest to longest.

- Ask your loved one to create different shapes using the strips of balsa wood, such as a square, rectangle, or trapezoid. You may need to provide them with pictures of these shapes to guide them.

- Create one or more rulers with the strips of balsa wood. Mark off inch increments on the strips and number them. Then, use the rulers to measure different objects.

- Have your loved one show a child how to do this activity.

Less Challenging

- To reduce the level of challenge, you can create a template. Trace each strip onto one piece of 36" cardstock to demonstrate the placement of each strip.

- Reduce the number of balsa strips. Instead of using six, start with three or four.

- Eliminate the idea of grading the strips and simply enjoy manipulating the different pieces of balsa wood.

- Do the entire activity with your loved one watching. Ask them for their suggestions as you grade the strips.

- Have your loved one watch as someone else, such as a grandchild, does the activity.

Youngest to Oldest

DESCRIPTION

This activity is a memory stimulator, with a family twist! The idea is to get four pictures of a loved one in the family at different ages, and have your family member place them in order, starting with the youngest and progressing to the oldest.

HOW TO

1. The first step is to decide who you want to be in the pictures. Whose picture would make your loved one smile: a grandchild, you, a niece or a nephew?

2. Next, start collecting pictures. You are going to need pictures of the designated person at four different points in time. Make sure that the pictures are of clearly different ages.

3. Once your have selected your pictures, enlarge them (8.5" x 11" works well).

4. Create number labels (1 - 4) to help sequence the pictures (see photo).

5. You are ready to begin. Demonstrate how to do the activity for your family member before you ask them to do it.

Whose picture would make your loved one smile?

TIPS

- It is important to pick pictures that are clearly different ages. In other words, you would not want to select a picture from age 12 and age 13. They most likely would look very similar and it would be difficult to determine which came first. Pictures from infancy, early childhood, teenage years, and adulthood would be the ideal separation if the person in the pictures was currently an adult. If not, make sure that the pictures are all very different looking and spread out across different ages as much as possible.

- Try to make the pictures all the same size. This is cleaner looking and easier to use.

- Be sure to select portraits without much background, if possible. Backgrounds add unnecessary clutter.

- Because we are creating activities for older adults, we would also suggest choosing pictures that are brightly colored. If the lighting was poor when a picture was taken, it could be difficult for your family member to see the face in the picture.

- You also can use pictures of your loved one's friends, pets, etc., if these bring smiles!

ADAPTATIONS

More Challenging

Select portraits without much background.

- Instead of having your family member place four pictures in order by age, have them work with six. If six proves to be too simple, do eight!

- Ignore the previous tip about using photos that are clearly different ages. You can increase the complexity by using photos that are closer in age.

- Have your family member first place the pictures in the correct sequential order, but then have them guess the ages in each of the photo. If you try this approach, we would suggest writing the ages on the backs of the photos to have cues available if needed.

- Do something with the photos after they have ordered them. Possibly you can frame each one, or you can have your family member make a collage with the four pictures. Use these pictures for the beginning of a new photo album that you can put together with the help of your family member.

Less Challenging

- Start off with only two pictures to place in the correct age sequence instead of four. If two seems too easy, add a third. You can start off smaller and build up to a higher number when and if it becomes appropriate.

- You also can create a template to provide some more cueing. Perhaps you can do some color-coding. Put a different colored border around each picture. Create matching colored blocks on the template. If your family member was struggling a bit with placing the pictures in the correct sequence according to age, then they could use that extra built in cue of the color matching to aid them. You could also number the backs of the pictures (1, 2, 3, 4) and number the template as well. This way, they can look on the back of each picture for the number and match it with the corresponding number on the template.

- Add the ages to the bottom of the pictures in permanent marker. This way, you are taking some of the guesswork out of the equation and they would just have to focus on placing the ages in the correct order.

- Just look at the pictures and chat about them.

Just look at the pictures and chat about them.

First to Last

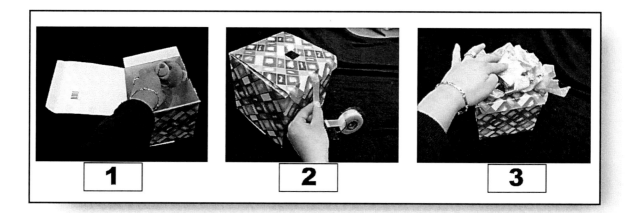

DESCRIPTION

This activity involves putting things in order. Your family member creates a story out of three pictures that, when placed in sequence, depict an event that your loved one enjoys. How great to be reminded of decorating a Christmas tree or the good old days of baking a cake in that stove that only worked half of the time!

HOW TO

Create a story that depicts an event your loved one enjoys.

1. The first step to doing this activity is to decide on a topic that is important to your family member. Were they a baker? Did they enjoy wrapping presents? Did they love decorating the tree at Christmas time or giving out Hannakah gelt to their grandchildren? Once you decide on some options, ask yourself if these stories can be told in three parts.

2. Collect three pictures that are representative of your chosen event and can easily tell a story when placed in order. For example, if your family member loved to bake, perhaps you could do a baking story. You could have a picture of someone mixing ingredients in a pan, followed by a picture of someone placing the pan in the oven, and conclude with a picture of someone pulling a baked cake out of the oven. You do not have to find three pictures that tell a story and fit together as described above. You can create them. Draft another helper, perhaps another family member or a family friend, to model for you and take some pictures. Now you have your story. It may be easier to make up your own pictures than to try to track down pictures that fit.

3. Get three index cards. On the first, print or type a large "1." On the second card, print or type a large "2." On the third, print or type a large "3" (see photo on previous page).

4. Once you have all of your pictures and have finished your cards, you are ready to begin. You can explain to your family member how to do the activity and demonstrate for them as well.

Help them to feel good about themselves.

TIPS

- If the activity displayed in the picture has a person in it, it is preferable to have the same person in all three of the pictures. This is less confusing and keeps the flow of the story going.

- Be sure that your pictures resemble an event or activity as your family member remembers it. If you choose to do a sequence on the wrapping of a present because your family member loves to wrap presents, then that seems like a great idea. However, the "in" thing to do today is to use gift bags instead of wrapping paper. Our point is to still use the wrapping paper in your pictures. Your family member remembers the days before gift bags and we would want to remind them of that memory, not introduce an entirely new concept that they may not be able to relate to.

- If your family member places the pictures in the wrong order, our suggestion would be to just let it go! Letting them think that they are the best picture sequencer out there is doing no damage and you are helping them to feel good about themselves. What could be wrong with that?

ADAPTATIONS

More Challenging

- To make this activity more of a challenge, you can add more pictures to the sequence. Instead of working with only three pictures, work with four or five, or even more. Work with as many as you want and that you think are appropriate for your family member to feel good about themselves.

- Another way to increase the complexity of this activity is to have your family member place the three cards in order as described above, but then ask them to make up the fourth step. What would come next?

Less Challenging

- To make this activity less challenging, you can use two pictures to order instead of three. You can always increase the complexity later. After they master the ordering of two pictures, you can add a third and a fourth picture.

- Another way to change the complexity of the activity is to number the pictures on the back. The first picture in the sequence would be numbered "1," the second would be numbered "2" and the third would be numbered "3." If your family member is struggling at all with the sequence, you could cue them to turn the cards over and match the numbers on the back with the numbers on the index cards. You can also number the pictures on the front if needed, in plain view. Again, enjoyment and engagement are goals. There is enough going on within this same activity that your family member will still reap the benefits of it, answers revealed or not!

- You can also approach the activity a bit differently to change the complexity. You can place all of the pictures in the correct sequence yourself, as your family member watches. Then, you can mix the pictures up again and have your family member give it a try.

- Also, you can put them in order as your family member watches and just discuss what is in the pictures, or the two of you can order them together.

- If you want to eliminate the idea of ordering pictures in a sequence all together, sit back, look at the pictures together, and relax! Let this activity work for you.

Create a Collage

DESCRIPTION

A collage, for our purposes, consists of a collection of pictures that are compiled together for display and enjoyment. This activity provides individuals with the freedom to create a piece of art that has significance and meaning to them.

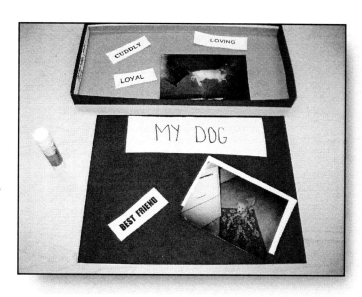

HOW TO

1. To make a collage, you will need a few supplies:

   a. **Background paper.** You can use whatever type and size of paper you want. (Cardstock, poster board, construction paper, etc.)

   b. **Non-toxic glue.** You have two glue options: a glue stick or craft glue that is poured into a plastic plate and applied with a thick-handled brush. Choose according to your family member's abilities. Asking someone at the craft store for suggestions on appropriate glue choices for these projects is always encouraged.

   c. **You will need a paper/plastic plate or shoebox lid.**

2. This next step is the fun part! Ask your family member what type of collage they would like to make. Give them some options to choose from, such as a flower collage, a pet collage, a color collage, etc. Your collages could include pictures, words, or both. For example, if you were doing a pet collage, you could have pictures of your pet and words that relate to that pet, such as "cute" and "cuddly." Or, you could make a word collage that would include all words that describe your loved one.

Create a piece of art that has significance and meaning.

3. Begin your search for the pictures and/or words that you will use. You can involve your family member in this process if they are able. Look through magazines together. Look through picture books that you wouldn't mind cutting up. If you are computer savvy, look on the computer for images that you can print if you have a color printer. Allow your family member to make the decisions if it is possible. If they cannot choose, then show them the pictures and ask which ones they like.

4. Once you and your family member have decided on some pictures, it is time to cut them out. We would suggest that you take the responsibility for this step, unless you are looking to make the activity a bit more challenging. If so, you can have them help you to the best of their ability.

Look through magazines together.

5. Place your pictures where they are easily viewable, perhaps in a shoebox lid or on a paper/plastic plate. This way, the options are there and your family member can look through the pictures and freely choose which ones they want to include.

6. Demonstrate. Show your family member how to spread (if using a glue stick) or brush a dab of glue on the background paper, pick out a picture, and then attach the picture to the glue.

7. Continue gluing and placing the pictures until the collage is the way your family member wants it. To make the collage look and feel more finished, you can frame it.

TIPS

- Allow your family member to pick which pictures they want to use and to decide where to place them if they can. Refrain from correcting your loved one or intervening unless they ask for or need assistance.

- Try to avoid presenting too many picture choices at one time for your family member. Place no more than four to five pictures in front of them at a time, and reduce this number if needed.

- If you are not sure what size collage would be appropriate for your family member, it is better to err on the side of caution. Start off small. If a small collage does not present enough of a challenge, you can always add more pictures or words at a later time.

- When cutting out the pictures, choose ones that are less busy. Pictures that show only one flower or one fruit, for example, would be ideal. Too much clutter in a picture can become overwhelming and frustrating.

- You may want to create collages at the same time, with you making one collage while your family member makes another.

ADAPTATIONS

More Challenging

- Have your family member be involved with more steps of this activity. Have them begin with picking out the pictures from magazines or other sources, followed by cutting them out, then gluing, etc. until the project is completed.

- Increase the size of the collage.

Less Challenging

- Have your family member do one step of this activity repetitively. For example, have them be the designated glue dabber or the picture picker.

Start out small. You can always add more pictures or words later.

- Do the whole activity with your loved one watching and include them by asking questions: "Do you think that this flower is pretty?" "Do you think that I should glue this word here?"

- Create a smaller collage.

- Provide more of a template. If you feel that the freedom to place the pictures or words anywhere would be confusing to your loved one, outline boxes on the background to guide where the pictures or words could be placed.

Make a Mosaic

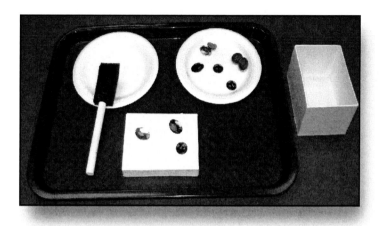

DESCRIPTION

This activity is another project to get those artistic, crafty juices flowing once again. Have you ever made a mosaic? If not, this is your chance to work with some rhinestones and help your family member create a mosaic art piece. Roll your sleeves up and get ready to be creative!

Get those artistic, crafty juices flowing once again.

HOW TO

1. To begin this activity, you will need some supplies. Once again, you should head to your local craft store. You are probably becoming a familiar face there by now! The following supplies will help you complete this activity:

    a. **Background/surface.** You can create a mosaic solely for artistic purposes. If you choose this approach, you can just purchase a piece of cardstock on which you will glue the rhinestones. However, if you would like to create something that is not only artistic but also functional, purchase a different material. For example, craft stores often have a vast selection of paper mache boxes of different shapes and sizes. These are very inexpensive, are often white or the color of a brown grocery bag, and are easy to work with. When you have finished the project, they can be used to put little things in, such as paper clips, or given away as gifts. Craft stores also have unfinished wood sections where you will find small wooden boxes. Working with wood may be a good option, especially for men.

    b. **Paper plates**. You will need two plates: one will hold your rhinestones and the other will be for your glue. The paper dishes can be disposed of once you are finished so you do not need to worry about scrubbing glue out of a container.

c. **Glue & Brush.** You will need non-toxic glue and a brush to apply the glue. You should ask someone at the craft store to suggest types of glue that would work for your project. A staff member at the craft store could also guide you towards a non-toxic glue product for wood. When selecting a brush, be sure to get one with a thicker handle so it will be a bit easier for your family member to grip.

d. **Rhinestones.** Select the largest rhinestones available to work with. You have a much greater chance of an older adult being able to manipulate a larger rhinestone than tiny ones. If it is at all possible for your family member to help you select the colors of the rhinestones they would like to use, that would be great. The selection could be quite expansive at the craft store, so you may need to narrow it down for them.

2. If you have access to a clutter-free table that is in a distraction-free (if there is such a thing!) area, set the activity up there. If your family member has limited mobility, bring the activity to them on a tray. Pour some glue into one of the paper plates and place this plate within your family member's reach. Put the brush in the glue. Place the rhinestones on the second dish and place it to the right of the glue dish. The glue should be first in line followed by the plate of rhinestones. Finally, place the background surface directly in front of your family member (see photo). Everything should be within easy reach.

3. Demonstrate the activity. The first step is to dip the brush in the glue. The second step is to generously coat the background surface (cardstock or box) with the glue. The final step is to adhere the rhinestones to the glue. If your family member cannot dig the rhinestones out of the dish, put them in their hand. Adapt it as needed to make the process go smoother for them. Focus on engagement and fun!

4. Have your family member (or yourself) continue gluing and adhering the rhinestones until the surface is covered or until the mosaic is as your family member wants it. This is their project, so let's keep it their decision. If they decide that it looks good before the surface is covered, so be it. And there you go! You have a mosaic piece of art or a mosaic box. Perhaps you can attach a tag that says "MADE TOGETHER BY... ." This way they will always be reminded that they made that box or piece of art together with their loving family member.

Roll your sleeves up and get ready to be creative!

TIPS

- If you are not sure what size box or cardstock would be appropriate for your family member, it is better to err on the side of caution. Start off small. If a small surface does not present enough of a challenge, you can always go bigger the next time or do a second project. It is better to start off too easy than too difficult. We want to avoid overwhelming anyone.

- If the rhinestones are difficult for your family member to manipulate, then perhaps you can take the same general principle and still construct a box or piece of art, but use something larger as your mosaic pieces. Craft stores have aisles full of options to choose from. In the unfinished wood sections, there are always wooden shapes; or in the craft foam section, there are foam shapes. Look around and select something that is thicker or larger.

- Allow your family member to be in the driver's seat as much as possible with this project. Allow them to pick the rhinestones for the mosaic and also allow them to decide where they want each rhinestone to go, if they can.

ADAPTATIONS

More Challenging

- To increase the challenge, go larger. You can increase the size of the box or cardstock.

- You can also change the complexity by presenting patterns that your family member can try to recreate with their mosaic. Give them a few simple patterns to choose from. You will have to create the patterns ahead of time, but if it brings a smile to your family member's face, this is time well spent.

- If you opted to use a paper mache box for this project, you can add challenge by having your family member paint the box before adding the rhinestones.

- If using a wooden box, it can be sanded. Gluing felt to the inside transforms this into a jewelry box. Be sure to ask staff at the craft store to provide you with wooden boxes that are safe for sanding.

Less Challenging

- Assuming the rhinestones are multicolored, you can make this activity less complex by making a template on the cardstock or the top of the box. Outline each rhinestone and color the outline in. Assuming that all the rhinestones will be the same size, your family member will be focusing on matching the color and shape on the template with the matching rhinestone piece.

- To further adapt the activity, keep all of the rhinestones the same size, shape, and color and create the template on the cardstock or the box top.

- You can reduce the complexity of the activity by reducing the steps they perform. You can apply the glue and your family member can place the rhinestones. Or, they can brush on the glue and you add the rhinestones. They can even just point to where they want the pieces to go, and you do the rest.

- Instead of creating a mosaic, you can purchase rhinestones of different colors and have your family member sort the rhinestones by color. Or, purchase rhinestones of different shapes or sizes and have them sort by size or shape.

- Have your family member tear pieces of construction paper into different shapes and glue them onto a background.

If it brings a smile to your family member's face, this is time well spent.

Decorate a Hat

DESCRIPTION

Does your loved one wear hats? Do you think that they would wear a hat if it reflected their own brand of creativity? This activity consists of giving new life to some old (or new) hats.

HOW TO

Give new life to some old (or new) hats.

1. Your first step to this activity is to gather your supplies:

   a. **A hat.** At the craft store, you can purchase visor hats that are made of craft foam. You can also purchase cotton baseball caps and fisherman hats. All of these hats are in the craft store because they are meant to be decorated. Additionally, they are not expensive.

   b. **Decorations for your hat.** While you are at the craft store looking for your hat, you could also search for decorations. You could purchase self-adhesive shapes made from craft foam. They also have a number of shapes that are not self-adhesive, but could work as well. You could also choose flowers, rhinestones, team logos, or whatever your family member finds interesting. If possible, bring them along and let them help choose what they'd like to put on their hat.

   c. **Glue and a brush.** You have to be picky about your glue here because you need glue that is non-toxic and will allow you to adhere things to fabric or craft foam. Ask workers at the craft store to help you select glue. You will also want to purchase (if you do not already have one) a thick-handled brush to apply the glue. Thicker handles allow for easier gripping, thus making it more likely that your family member can help with the gluing process.

   d. **A plastic dish.** You will need a dish to pour your glue into.

2. Pour some of the glue into your dish and place it near your family member's dominant hand. Place your brush in the glue and place the hat directly in front of where your family member is sitting. Put your decoration items in front of your family member so they can see the different options. Do not make the options too plentiful, which may add frustration. Five to seven items are best to try at first. You could always add more or take some away.

3. Demonstrate. This is a three-step process of dipping the brush in glue, dabbing the glue on the spot of choice on the hat, and putting the decoration item on the glued area.

4. After demonstrating, allow your family member to proceed with the project. Provide guidance as needed, but allow them to make this hat their own. Whatever they create is perfectly acceptable. There is no right or wrong way to decorate something.

5. If your family member is experiencing any memory problems, you can find a way to let them remember what they have created. This way, they can feel that sense of accomplishment and pride over and over again. One suggestion would be to write on the inside of the hat in permanent marker, "Made Together By…" Then, when they see or are shown that message, they can feel good about their accomplishment again.

TIPS

There is no right or wrong way to decorate something.

*   Glue can be tricky. Depending on the type of glue and decorations that you are adhering, you may also need to put glue on the back of the items (rhinestone, shape, etc.) as well as on the hat. If this is the case, perhaps it would be a good idea for you to be the glue dabber to prevent any frustration.

*   We would not recommend throwing these hats in the washer. Chances are, you would not have your decorations still attached when they came out. If your loved one adores the hat and wears it constantly, perhaps you can try hand washing it or spot cleaning it, or making a second, "back-up" hat.

*   Keep this age-appropriate. It is critical to respect their status as adults. We would not suggest choosing any decoration item that could seem child-like.

- Be aware! You are probably going to be working with small objects. If your family member has some memory deficits and forgets what the rhinestones, shapes, or flowers are, they may think they are candy and place them in their mouth. We do not want that to happen. It helps to start an activity by describing what the objects are, and to demonstrate their use before giving them to the person with memory problems. However, if you feel that putting things in their mouth is a realistic possibility with your family member, please choose another activity.

- Make hats that they can give as gifts, especially to grandchildren.

ADAPTATIONS

More Challenging

Make this a doable activity for your loved one.

- Use more decoration items. Maybe they can work with ten at a time. Or, you can make the design a little more complex. Instead of just gluing shapes, flowers, or rhinestones to a hat, have your family member add some decorative paint to the hat as well.

- Create a coordinating miniature tote bag, also sold at the craft stores.

- You can also create a picture frame. Pick up an unfinished wooden picture frame, and cover it with your chosen decorations. If you are going to work with wood, you also need to pick up an appropriate non-toxic glue. Ask someone at the craft store for guidance.

Less Challenging

- As we have mentioned a number of times throughout this manual, eliminate steps if necessary. Make yourself the designated glue dipper, glue dabber, or decoration adherer to reduce the number of steps. Make this a doable activity for your loved one.

- Use a shirt instead of a hat to decorate. Put outlines of the decoration items in permanent marker on the shirt. This way, they have more of a guide for placing the items.

- Let them make a hat together with a grandchild.

Colored Sand Bottles

DESCRIPTION

This activity allows the artistic talent of your family member to flow! It involves pouring colored sand through a funnel into bottles for the purpose of having some fun together and adding décor to your loved one's room.

HOW TO

1. Before doing this activity, you will need some supplies:

Allow the artistic talent to flow!

   a. **Plastic or glass bottles.** (If your loved one lives in a facility, be sure to get the staff's okay if you want to use glass.) You may even have a couple of these around your house. If not, go to your handy craft store. They sell empty bottles for very little money. You often see bottles with corks in them at craft stores. They come in varying sizes. The bottles with corks are ideal because sand can definitely get messy if the bottle were to spill over with the sand inside. You also would want a clear bottle so the colored sand effect will show through. Avoid the frosted clear glass because the frosted glass will mute the effect of the colored sand. So again, the ideal bottle will be a clear bottle with a cork in it.

   b. **Plastic funnel.** You can probably go to your kitchen for this. If not, go to the dollar store. You just need a funnel that fits securely into the bottle that you are going to use.

c. **Colored sand.** You can get the colored sand at the craft store as well. It is pretty cheap so you will not have a big expense there either. We would suggest a maximum of three different colors. Because your family member will be constructing this bottle, we do not want to overwhelm them with too many choices. It is a good idea to get three colors that contrast from one another (such as yellow, blue and red). The contrasting colors will hopefully help your family member see the different options. As always, we would suggest involving your family member as much as possible. Get their color preferences for the sand, but give them some colors to choose from first. If they are at the craft store with you, make some suggestions that will help them narrow down the choices.

d. **Containers that would hold the sand.** Clear plastic cups can be used, as long as your family member can see the top edge of the cup. You would want each color of sand to be in its own container. This way it is easier for your family member to pour the sand. If needed, you can label the container with the name of the color.

2. Once you have all of your supplies, you are ready to set up. Set the different colors in a row facing your family member. Be sure to place the containers of sand by your family member's dominant hand (right if right-handed and left if left-handed) so they are within reach.

Remember to start off small.

3. You are now ready to begin. The idea is to fill the bottle with the sand to form color layers. If your family member wants the bottle only one color, that's fine too. Your job is to first demonstrate how to pour the sand through the funnel. After you demonstrate, your job is to hold the funnel in place on the top of the bottle while they pour.

4. Encourage your family member to continue filling the bottle with sand by pouring it through the funnel, alternating colors if desired.

TIPS

- Remember to start off small. The bottle selection is sometimes quite vast at the craft store. Pick one that is smaller to begin with. You do not want one that is microscopic, but definitely one that is not large.

- Ideally, the bottle can sit on the table so it is level and your family member can work with it there. However, to work with the bottle on the table, your family member would have to reach up a little. Obviously some older adults do not have the ability to reach up like that. If this is the case, put a tray on their lap and set the bottle on the tray. You will have to work double time because you may have to have one hand on the bottle and one on the funnel in order to make this project doable for them. If your family member is in bed, you may be able to use an overbed table or breakfast tray to set the materials on.

- Once your family member finishes the sand bottle, it is a good idea to place it where it cannot get knocked over, such as on a shelf versus an end table. If you used a bottle with a cork, squirt some glue on the top of the sand and the edges of the cork before you seal the bottle. This will hold the sand and cork in the bottle more firmly.

Do a design with the sand.

ADAPTATIONS

More Challenging

- As always, you can change the complexity level of the activity by going bigger. You can always choose a larger bottle. You can always do more than one bottle. Going larger always ups the stakes! Or, you can add more colors of sand.

- Another way to alter the complexity of this activity is to do a design with the sand instead of just adding different colored layers of sand. You can continue to add the different colors of sand, but you would then take something like a chopstick and poke it down along the inside edges of the bottle, which would create designs.

Have your family member be the color coordinator.

• Another way to shake things up a bit is to add beads to the bottle. You can alternate between layers of colored sand and layers of beads. You would want beads that could fit through the funnel so you could follow the same process. They would be placed in a container or cup and poured through the funnel just as the sand was. You would want to pour enough beads that they form a barrier or dam in a sense. This way, when you pour the next layer of sand, the beads will block the sand from seeping through and mixing with the other layers below.

Less Challenging

• To create a less challenging activity, you can have your family member be the designated color coordinator. Instead of having them pour, you can be the pourer, and they will tell you which color goes next and tell you when to stop pouring each color. This still gives them a role and allows them to control the design of the bottle, still making this their project.

• To reduce the complexity level, you can also reduce the number of colors involved with the project. Instead of working with three colors, work with two. Or, work with one. You can still do the activity and have the bottle be only one color.

• Another alternative is to do the entire project by yourself with your family member sitting next to you watching you do it, and you asking for feedback from them. This still  keeps them involved. You are asking them for instructions and feedback or comments, but they are not doing the physical end of things.

Folding and Stuffing Mailers

DESCRIPTION

This activity gives your loved one the chance to pitch in and help. This may be especially meaningful if they've worked in office settings. It consists of folding papers, letters, flyers, etc., stuffing them in envelopes and delivering them. The content of the envelopes is what elevates this activity to new heights! You can really create a meaningful experience for your loved one by creating opportunities for them to do something wonderful for someone else.

HOW TO

1. The first step to creating this activity is deciding what you are going to put in your envelopes. If you happen to have real flyers that need to be put in envelopes...great! You already have a useful, purposeful activity planned. Many organizations may have flyers that would fit your needs and are looking for volunteers to help prepare them for mailing. However, if you do not have real flyers that truly require stuffing, then you can get creative. Our suggestion is to try something that will put a smile on someone's face. How about flyers that say "Have a Nice Day," "Have a Safe Holiday Season," or "We Love Our Troops?" You can create letters or flyers that say anything. If possible, get your family member's input. Throw out a couple of suggestions and let them choose.

2. If you need to create your own flyers and have access to a computer, print them up on your printer. Or, you can print them in marker on construction paper. If your family member can help create the flyers, then bring them on board. If they cannot help with the actual construction of the flyers or letters, ask for their input on how your message looks, such as if it should be larger, smaller, brighter, etc.

Give your loved one the chance to pitch in and help.

3. You will also need envelopes for this project. Plain white envelopes will work fine.

4. The next step is to set up. Prepare for only one step at a time. Since the first step is folding the flyers, place the pile of unfolded flyers in a basket or in a container. Have a second container or basket available to put the flyers in once your family member has finished folding them. Prepare an example flyer folded up in half or in thirds, depending on the size of your flyer and envelopes.

Use your own creativity.

5. Now that you've finished folding, your next step is stuff your envelopes. You will now need three containers: one with the folded flyers, one with envelopes, and an empty one for the finished product. If you feel that having all three containers in front of your family member will be confusing, remove the one with the folded flyers. You can be in charge of that pile. When they are ready for a new flyer, you can hand them one. Before you ask your family member to stuff the envelopes, make sure that you do a demonstration. Never expect them to do a task without demonstrating it first.

6. The final and most meaningful step of this activity is delivery. If you created a "Have a Nice Day" flyer, who will be the lucky recipient? If your relative lives in a nursing home (or in assisted living or attends adult day care), what a perfect place to deliver a thoughtful message! You should first clear it with the activity director or someone in charge, but assuming you get the green light, you and your family member can walk through the halls and deliver them. If your relative does not live in a nursing home or attend any day programs, then there must be one nearby. Scout them out and talk to someone about delivering your message. You can use your own creativity, but the point of this activity is to help your family member do something that makes them feel good. It also serves as a reminder that, regardless of the difficulties they are experiencing, they still have the ability to make people smile.

TIPS

- This activity does not have to be completed in one day. If you spread it out, it can be your project for the week! Your family member can possibly fold half of the flyers one day and finish folding another day. The stuffing can also be divided in half. You can spread it out however you want, depending on your loved one and their attention span, abilities, and interest.

- Determine the number of flyers depending on your family member. Again, if you start off small, you can always increase at a later time.

- When you're doing this activity, eliminate clutter and distraction in your workspace. If you are at a table, clear the table. If you are nearby a TV, keep it turned off. Distractions interfere with attention and focus on an activity.

ADAPTATIONS

The point is engagement and meaning.

More Challenging

- You can increase the difficulty of this activity by adding additional steps or details after the folding and stuffing have been completed. You can add stickers or labels, or you can have your family member write out the names of the recipients on the front of the envelopes. You can add extras any way you want. Just be sure to do one step at a time and not overwhelm your family member.

- You can also increase the challenge by adding more flyers.

Less Challenging

- To make this activity less challenging, you can remove steps. Have your family member only do one step repetitively. They can do all of the folding or all of the stuffing. Or, if need be, they can just hand you the flyers from the basket and you do the rest. The point is engagement and meaning. It doesn't matter how many steps are done.

- If your family member can read well, create an instruction sheet to place on the table. (Step 1: Take a flyer. Step 2: Fold it in half, etc.) Keep the instructions short and simple.

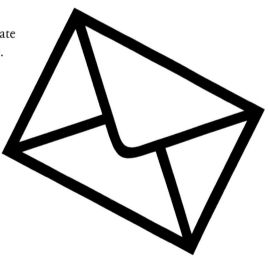

Making a Date

DESCRIPTION

Remember when someone last called and arranged for a date with you? No matter where you went, you felt very special because someone expressed a desire to spend time with you. Would you like to join your loved one for a night out, maybe dinner or a quick stop at a local coffee shop? Older adults with memory impairments may not initiate dates anymore because it has become too complicated to do the inviting. However, that does not mean that you cannot arrange for a date with them. This next activity is about giving your family member a date to look forward to on a regular basis.

Give your family member a date to look forward to on a regular basis.

HOW TO

1. When we refer to a "date" we are really referring to a designated time to be together. This could be a meal or a trip to a coffee shop, but it really can be anything. Choose two activities that you and your loved one may have enjoyed in the past. Think of activities that would still be appropriate now and could be accomplished without frustration. Some date ideas might be going to a library or sunroom to read a favorite book together, sharing a grandchild's report card, looking at a picture album, attending a concert or a local play, or maybe having a beer at a local pub (if it's medically allowed).

2. Present your two choices for a date and invite your loved one to choose between the two.

3. Set a regular time and once a week or once a month, you and your loved one go on your date. You can change the place that you go or what you do, but the point is to do something special on an ongoing basis. This gives your family member something special to look forward to and focus on. If they cannot remember the date, then it is a nice surprise when you go to take them. If your family member cannot leave the house or their facility due to medical issues, set something up for them there. (See our adaptations section.)

TIPS

- Food can always add a special flare to a visit. If you decide to stay in, a beverage and a favorite snack are always good beginnings. How about an afternoon tea at the kitchen table with a selection of different flavors to choose from?

- Don't forget to include friends and extended family members in your dates. This does not have to be a one-on-one interaction between you and your family member. It's actually a perfect opportunity for others to be able to visit without having to plan. Grandchildren are always wonderful additions to a visit. They can be very creative. An older grandchild can share a lunch or a favorite story.

- Plan ahead. If you plan on your date being a trip to the park, check ahead of time to locate the wheelchair accessible ramps or make sure that there is a handicapped bathroom facility.

- To aid your family member in remembering your special date, you can hang up a monthly calendar, marking in red these special dates and placing this calendar where your loved one can see it.

- When choosing an outing to a restaurant, park, mall, etc., perhaps you should go at a less busy time of day. If it is a busy time of year, such as the holidays, a quiet date at home may be the perfect option.

- Do not be discouraged if the date doesn't go according to plan the first time. If you think about it, how often do dates really go as planned?

An older grandchild can share a lunch or a favorite story.

ADAPTATIONS

More Challenging

- Involve your loved one in the planning. They can help in choosing places, times, and activities.

- Create special invitations to send out as reminders if others are involved in your date.

- If your date is at home for a meal, you can create simple menus for it. You could even dust off your loved one's favorite china and silver and use it to set the table.

Begin with that special tea or lemonade at the kitchen table.

- Fill in a monthly calendar together marking special upcoming dates in red. You also could place stickers or stars to mark the special events.

Less Challenging

- Begin with a simple, uncomplicated idea and increase the level of complexity over time. For instance, begin with that special tea or lemonade at the kitchen table or in their room once a week at 3:30. Over time, you may wish to plan an outing to the teahouse.

- Choose activities that do not require you to organize too much. Take your loved one to a movie. The entertainment is the movie, so you do not have to worry about providing it.

Gift Wrap

DESCRIPTION

This activity is ideal for holiday time. If you are looking for an activity that will keep your family member involved with the preparations for the holiday season, have them create some wrapping paper for your gifts. This activity requires paper, paint and/or stamps, and some tender loving care!

HOW TO

1. Your first step is deciding what type of wrapping paper you would like to create. As always, you want to make your family member a part of this process as much as possible. Your job will be to give them some options. If you have some Christmas presents to wrap, possibly you would like to make candy cane or Christmas tree wrapping paper. If you have some Chanukah presents to wrap, you can make Star of David paper or dreidel wrapping paper. If you want winter paper, make snowflakes. Do not present your family member with too many selections, but give them a few to choose from. This is their project, so it is important to always keep that in mind.

2. Your second step is to gather your supplies. Your local craft store should have everything that you need.

   a. **You will need paper.** There are several paper selections that would probably be appropriate. Read labels and ask someone at the craft store for assistance, especially if you plan to use paint. You would need a paper that is durable enough for paint. Avoid papers that are too thick, such as construction paper or card stock. If you are a gift bag person, create some specially designed tissue paper to stuff your gift bags with. Buy whatever color you want, but lighter colors would probably be easier to decorate. Also, if you plan to decorate tissue paper, you would probably want to steer clear of paint and stick to the stamps. Tissue paper is not strong enough to hold paint well.

Keep your family member involved with the preparations for the holiday season.

b. **You will also need stencils, stamps or both!** Decide on the decorating materials to use based on your family member's abilities. The stencils would require paint and may be a little more complex than the stamping. Once you have decided on stencils or stamps, you can choose which ones. If your family member wanted to make winter wonderland paper, for example, pick out a stencil or stamp of a snowflake, or of anything linked to winter. The craft stores typically have a large selection of both stencils and stamps, so you should not have any problems finding options.

c. **If you have opted to try out the stencils, you will need non-toxic paint and brushes.** Pick out whatever color(s) of paint that you want, but be sure that the color(s) of the paint contrasts with the color of the paper. When selecting brushes, pick ones that have thick handles, since these will be easier for your family member to grip.

d. **If you opted for the stamps, you will need ink pads.** Again, as with the paint, pick whatever color you want, but be sure that the ink contrasts with the color of the paper you will be using.

e. **If you are using the stencils and paint, you will also need paint dishes to squirt the paint into.** Plastic dishes would work fine. If you put the paint in a dish, your family member will have an easier time using it.

3. Now that you have your supplies, your next step is set up. Place the blank paper in front of your family member. If you are using the stencil and paint, place the stencil on the paper. Your family member should only have to put a paintbrush to it.

4. Once you have everything set up, you demonstrate how to use the stamp and inkpad or the paint and stencil. Allow your family member to choose where they want to stamp or stencil next. Your role is to guide them. If they are stenciling, you would probably want to hold the stencil down for them while they fill it in with paint.

TIPS

- Be sure to remind your loved one who made the special wrapping paper by writing on their completed sheets, "Made Especially for You by Grandma" (or Grandpa, etc.).

- Ask someone at the craft store about making stamps out of fruits or vegetables.

- If you like the idea of using the stamps or prefer the selection of stamps at the craft store over the collection of stencils, but also prefer the paint, then buy the stamp and the paint. Instead of ink, you can use paint on the stamp. Rather than dipping the stamp in paint, use your paintbrush to put some paint onto the stamp. This way you can have better control over the amount of paint that you put on the stamp. This obviously adds a step to the activity, so you can make this step your responsibility.

ADAPTATIONS

More Challenging

- To make this activity more of a challenge, you can add some complexity to your design. Instead of using paint with the stencil, you can use glitter. First, trace the stencil in marker to form some boundary lines. Next, remove the stencil and decorate inside the outlined shape with the glitter. For the glitter to stick, you would also need glue. (As always, use non-toxic materials.) The addition of glue and glitter would add extra steps, thus adding challenge! You would want to be sure to use glitter in a jar with a sprinkle top to reduce mess. You would also want to pour some glue into a plastic dish or plate and plan on applying it with a brush to make it easier for your family member to help with this step. Alternatively, you could use a large glue stick to apply the glue.

- You can also add complexity to any project by increasing the size of the project. In this case, increase the amount of wrapping paper that you create.

- Change up the design, or throw some birthday wrap into the mix.

- Make some matching cards to accompany your specially-designed wrap.

Less Challenging

- Reduce the steps for your family member. They can be the designated stamper and you prepare the stamp by covering it with ink. Or, you paint the stencil while they pick out the spot where it will be placed each time.

- You can also always decrease the challenge by using smaller paper and wrapping smaller presents.

- Use this technique to create a holiday card instead.

Welcome Baskets

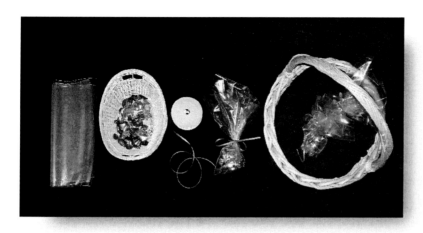

DESCRIPTION

The idea behind this next activity is to create a basket of individually wrapped treats that will eventually be used as welcome gifts. If you are interested in hearing more, please keep reading!

HOW TO

Great if your loved one lives in a nursing home

1. This activity is great if your loved one lives in a nursing home because you can give the nursing home the welcome basket. They could offer a treat to potential families exploring the facility or even to staff as a little token of appreciation for their hard work. The first step is the fun part. You need to decide what type of candy that you would like to place in each treat bag. You would not want to give out any candy that tastes bad, so perhaps you and your loved one could do some tasting! It is a tough job, but someone has to do it. (Only do this if your family member's diet permits.)

2. Your second step would be to gather some supplies. You do not really need much:

    a. **The most important supply is the candy.** We would suggest buying candies that are individually wrapped.

    b. **Bags for the candy.** You really can choose any type of bag that you want. Our suggestion would be the miniature cellophane treat bags that you can find at party stores or even craft stores. They are typically not expensive and often times come in packages of up to 25-30.

    c. **Ribbon to tie the bags.** This does not have to be anything expensive. Buy a spool of any color, preferably chosen by your family member.

    d. **A basket to hold the individual bags.** You probably have a basket lying around your house somewhere. Dig it out. If not, craft stores often have a large collection. Garage sales may also feature baskets. Have your loved one help pick out the basket, if possible.

3. Organize an assembly line of sorts. Put the candy in a bowl or basket on a table. Place a pile of bags next to the candy and a pile of ribbons next to the bags and at the end of the line would be the basket. So, from left to right, you would have the candy, followed by the bags, ribbons, and basket, respectively. Since there are four separate items and essentially four tasks to this process, it would probably be a good idea to have your family member focus on only two tasks. We would not want to overwhelm them. They could pick up a few pieces of candy and place them in the bag, and you could tie the ribbon around the bag and place it in the basket. (Be sure to disinfect the hands of everyone who will be handling the candy.)

4. You are now ready to start creating your treat bags and filling your basket with them.

5. Once you have filled your basket, deliver it to the nursing home office.

TIPS

- If you would like to bring your welcome basket anywhere outside of the nursing home, call first and ask permission. You want to make sure that they can accept your welcome basket before you make the trip out there.

- You should consider dietary restrictions when selecting candy. If the facility offers the candy to potential families considering them as a future home for their loved one, a variety would probably be best. Besides regular candy, you may have to look for some sugar-free and low sodium candies too. The families can pick what they and their loved one are permitted to eat.

- If you are compiling your candy basket around a specific holiday, you could make more holiday-oriented selections. If it is around Valentine's Day, chocolate hearts would probably go over well. If it is around Thanksgiving time, candy corns sometimes come individually wrapped. Choose whatever you and your family member want.

- If candy does not appeal to you or your family member, put something else as gifts in the welcome basket.

ADAPTATIONS

More Challenging

- You and your family member can still create the welcome basket full of treats, but you can also decorate the basket.

- Create a sweet poem to accompany the treats.

- Instead of creating a welcome basket, you can keep the treats and use them for a holiday dinner. Have your family member help you create individual name labels to attach to each bag and use them instead of place cards. This way your guests will know where to sit.

- Another way to make this a little more challenging is to make it a bigger project. Instead of creating a single basket of treats, create treat bags for trick-or-treaters at Halloween time.

Less Challenging

Create a sweet poem to accompany the treats.

- Have your family member do only one step out of the four step process, such as placing the finished treat bags in the welcome basket.

- Instead of using cellophane bags and ribbon, use something that does not need to be put together. There are treat or favor boxes that you often find in the craft stores near the bridal sections. These are often used to hold candy favors at weddings. They are not very costly and do not need to be assembled. You would just have to put the candy in them.

Recording a Message

DESCRIPTION

Can you ever place a price on the sound of your loved one's voice or the sight of their smile? This activity captures that voice and smile in a video. We all know how important it is to keep in touch with those that we hold dear. How would you feel about recording a video message from your family member for someone that lives afar?

Hello my dear!
I just wanted to say hello and let you know that I am thinking of you. Give my love to everyone!

HOW TO

1. This may seem like an obvious first step, but ask your family member about this first. Many people are very self-conscious about being recorded and if your family member is one of those people, then we would definitely not suggest proceeding. Regardless of what difficulties they are experiencing, we always try our best to respect their opinions and honor their choices.

Capture voices and smiles in a video.

2. Talk to your family member about who will be the lucky recipient of the message. Will it be a grandchild, a niece, a nephew, etc.? Whoever it is, they are in for a pleasant surprise!

3. To do this activity, you obviously need to have access to a video recorder and know how to use it. If you need a refresher course, perhaps you can team up with someone that can give you a quick how-to lesson.

4. Gather all of your players for the recording. If you have a tripod to place your recorder on, then you only need yourself and your family member. However, if you do not have a tripod, you will need an additional person to do the recording. You will be the interviewer and will be asking your family member a question that leads to their favorite joke, story, or piece of advice. You need to make sure that you ask a leading question that cues your family member to tell a familiar story. This is important, because our goal is not to ask your family member to think on their feet necessarily. We want to tap into something that you know they remember well, perhaps a story or advice or a message that you have heard repetitively.

5. Bring your family member to a quiet, private space so they can feel less

inhibited or self-conscious about being recorded.

Start a video library of all the messages.

6. Prior to recording, it is probably a good idea to do a demo. This may give your family member a better sense of how this will go. After you have demonstrated, you can practice a couple of times to make sure that your family member feels comfortable with the process.

TIPS

•   The best tip that we can give is to keep it short and sweet! As always, we do not want to overwhelm. This is the first video and everyone gets better at something with more practice, so possibly later videos can be a bit lengthier. If your family member has a favorite joke that is only one line, then your message will only be one line. Regardless of the length, this video goes straight to the heart.

•   Because you are doing a recording, you want your mock recording studio to have bright lighting. So, when picking out the recording location, be alert as to the brightness of the lights or whether you have some outlets around to add extra lighting. You should encourage your family member to wear bright clothing so the image is crisper and clearer. Also, they may want to dress up for the occasion. Women might enjoy putting on makeup and a special outfit. Men might want to shave and wear a tie.

•   Have fun with this! Do not worry about this being perfect. The message recipient is not going to be critiquing the video, just enjoying it. And the idea is for you and your loved one to enjoy making it.

ADAPTATIONS

More Challenging

- Make a regular activity out of video recorded messages. Record one monthly and keep a copy of every video message that you send out. Then, start a video library of all the messages. What a great keepsake to always treasure! Have your family member help set up and catalogue items for the library.

- Bring the grandchildren into the video and have them interview your family member with more random questions. This will certainly up the stakes because they will have to answer questions on the spot! Or, for an even greater challenge, have your family member interview the grandchildren, or have your family member interview you. You would not want to try this adaptation with someone that would struggle with it, of course. You know your family member the best so you can make a decision as to whether or not this would be appropriate.

- If you are truly a tech wizard and are living in the computer fast lane, then possibly you can even introduce your family member to instant messaging with a loved one that lives afar. Whatever you think will work for you, go ahead and give it a try!

Less Challenging

- How about if you and your family member appear in the video together and you do the talking? You can tell your family member's favorite joke, story, or piece of advice.

- If you do not have access to a video recorder or think that it just would not go over well, how about an audiotape instead? Rather than videotaping your family member giving the message, you can audiotape them.

- Or, you can eliminate the idea of recording all together and write a letter instead (see next activity).

Bring the grandchildren into the video.

Note Writing

DESCRIPTION

This activity allows your family member to stay connected with others who live far from home. The purpose is simply to write letters to loved ones.

HOW TO

Stay connected with loved ones.

1. There are not many steps to prepare for this activity. You will need paper and something to write with. Use whatever type of paper that you want, such as stationary, notebook paper, etc. We are assuming that you are physically writing the letter, but if your family member is assisting with this task, be sure to use a pen or marker that's thick (for easier gripping). Additionally, we suggest using light-colored stationary and dark ink.

2. Ask your family member who they would like to write a letter to. Give them a few suggestions to choose from, such as a grandchild, a niece, etc.

3. Ask your family member what they would like to say in their letter. Spend some time with them on this part, because it's the most significant. Allow your family member to control the content as much as possible. Give them suggestions, but let them choose which ones to use. You may have to print out suggestions and let them point to their preference. That's okay. However, put them in the driver's seat. Again, this is their project and we want to encourage them to be a part of it as much as they can be. Once you finish writing the letter, let your family member help you address it. They also can assist by putting on the stamp and sealing the envelope.

4. Send the letter! Perhaps your loved one can come with you to the post office or mailbox. This by itself can be a "mini-outing." Keeping in touch with out-of-towners becomes difficult for individuals who are increasingly struggling with the challenges of aging, especially when their problems are memory-related. This particular activity helps your family member stay connected to someone who lives far away. This is also a perfect opportunity for you and your loved one to join forces and create something special. Additionally, think how wonderful your family member will feel if they get a response. Seize this opportunity!

TIPS

- If your family member ever seems overwhelmed or worried during the activities, or you sense even slight frustration beginning to mount, provide as much guidance as needed. You may need to put the activity aside for a while and then take it up again later.

- We recommend that you let your family member do as much of the activity as possible. However, we understand the types of deficits associated with memory problems, and that those deficits may prevent your loved one from expressing their preferences. We just want them to have the option of making choices if they are able.

ADAPTATIONS

More Challenging

- To increase the complexity of this activity, you can add additional steps. Instead of using notebook paper or ready-made stationary for your letter, you can have your family member help you decorate your own stationary. Take regular notebook paper and, together with your loved one, add some stickers to it. You can also decorate it through stamping or even coloring. This will add your family member's special personal touch.

- You can also have your family member create a collection of stationary with the intention of giving them as a specially-designed present. They would create several pieces of stationary instead of just one piece. Take the pile of stationary that they created and tie a bow around it for a present to their grandchild or their niece or to anyone.

Help your family member stay connected to someone who lives far away.

- Depending on your family member's abilities, you could also increase the complexity of this project by having your family member physically take part in the writing of the letter, beyond dictating to you what to write. Again, this is only an option if they are capable of helping with this component of the project.

- There is one additional adaptation that can make this project a little more challenging. Instead of writing a letter together, you can send a message from your family member on an audiotape. If you have access to a tape recorder, perhaps you can record them relaying a message to the recipient. It is a good idea to make some notes for your family member to have in front of them in case they need some cues as they record their message.

Less Challenging

- Instead of writing a letter, send a card with a message already inscribed inside. This way, you can either have your family member simply sign the card, if they are able, or you can add a simple one-liner. You and your family member are still experiencing the rewarding feeling of sending something personal to someone you love.

- You still write the letter, but instead of having your family member help you with the content, you do that on your own. Just tell them what you are writing as you do it. This still includes them in this activity and allows them to feel that they are a part of this. When you have finished writing the letter, you would of course sign it from the both of you.

- You can also have them sit in your company as you write the letter and tell them what you are writing, but they will prepare the envelope by adding the stamp and an adhesive return label when you have finished. They could insert the letter in the envelope if they are able.

A Memory Basket

DESCRIPTION

Talking about special memories from the past is a favorite activity among older adults. What if you captured a piece of your loved one's memories in a basket? This next activity will help you to create a memory basket with the help of your family member.

HOW TO

1. Select a basket. If you don't already have a basket, they are available at craft stores or department stores. Baskets often make appearances at garage sales as well. If your family member happens to have a basket that they have had for years and it means something to them, by all means, use that!

2. Deciding on the contents of the basket is very significant. Sit down with your family member and decide together what should go into it. Present them with options. You may be aware of some potential items for the basket. Present them to your loved one and see their reaction. This could be a picture, a bracelet, a statuette, a letter, etc. Place a handful of items that seem particularly important to them into the basket.

3. Sit down with your loved one and show them the items in the basket. Encourage them to take the objects out of the basket and hold them. Give them time to grasp these special items and to remember. Reminisce. Enjoy hearing about the memories these items can bring out. You can even make this an ongoing activity.

4. Add to your basket or change its contents to include more or different items.

Capture a piece of your loved one's memories in a basket.

TIPS

- Try not to keep too many items in the basket at one time because you don't want to make it overwhelming for your loved one.

- If possible, let your family member help choose the basket.

ADAPTATIONS

More Challenging

- To make this activity more challenging, you could create baskets regularly, such as themed baskets that are in sync with the holidays. For example, you could create a basket around Thanksgiving and include items such as a special pumpkin pie recipe.

- Or, you can create some custom-made items. For example, you and your family member could create a "Those That I Hold Dear" booklet to add to the basket. With the help of your loved one, write a paragraph about each person that they hold close to their heart. Include a picture next to each person's paragraph. Compile these into a booklet.

- A more complex task is for you and your family member to construct a family tree for your basket.

- You can also prepare cards with the help of your loved one, if possible, that explain the significance of each item. Then you can leave the basket out with the accompanying cards, and your family member can read about the items when you are not around.

- Another option is to increase the complexity by decorating the basket that you use. You can decorate with any number of things, such as ribbon or flowers.

- Finally, you can take your family member to garage sales to shop for baskets or other bargains.

Construct a family tree for your basket.

Less Challenging

- To make this activity less challenging, have your family member sit with you and watch as you put together the memory basket. They are still a part of the activity, even if they are not making any decisions, but simply observing. You can tell them about the items and place the items in their hands, or let them touch the items without holding them.

- You can also reduce the complexity of this activity by keeping only one item in the basket at a time. You could change the item every week.

The Guestbook

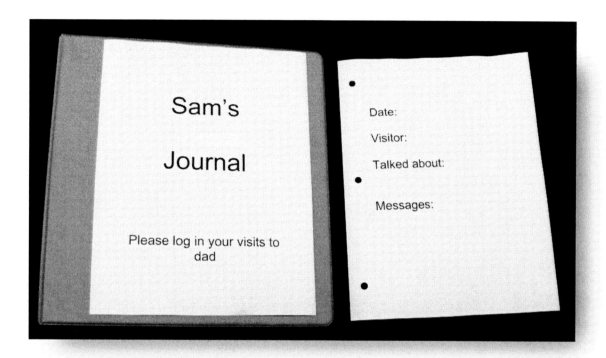

Sam's

Journal

Please log in your visits to
dad

Date:

Visitor:

Talked about:

Messages:

DESCRIPTION

This activity can be one to reflect on and enjoy.

Not every activity has to have lots of materials and layers of complexity. This next activity can be one to simply reflect on and enjoy. Doesn't it feel good to have a family member or friend come for a visit or give you a call out of the blue? These visits or phone calls suggest that someone was thinking of you. But someone experiencing memory deficits may not remember the visits and phone calls. A guestbook will serve as a reminder of all of the visitors that pass through and all of the phone calls that are made to your loved one.

HOW TO

1. The first step is to get a book to write in. It doesn't have to be anything fancy, or it can be. What would your family member enjoy? Would they prefer a fancy, decked-out book with all the fixings? Would a simple notebook be more their style? Or, would loose-leaf notebook pages in a binder suit them just fine? Use whatever you think would fit with your loved one's personality.

Create a book that captures phone calls, visitors, and inquiries.

2. Once you have decided on a book, label the cover. The words on the label should make sense to your family member. Show them the book you will be using, tell them what it will be used for, and ask them what they would like to call it. Then use the label they give you for the guestbook. It helps to call the book something simple that is easy to decipher, such as "Dad's Visitors" or "Dad's Guestbook." Perhaps it is better if you put their name, "Beverly's Visitors" or "Sam's Guestbook." Or, use their first and last name. Use whatever name or nickname they would recognize as being their own. The idea is to make the label self-explanatory. You want them to be aware that it belongs to them and it is about their visitors. If you think that your family member would have a hard time understanding that this book belongs to them, put their picture as a young adult on the front in addition to their name.

3. Decide on a place to keep the guestbook. You want it to be in a place that your family member cannot miss. Maybe there's a table by their door that holds their keys. Maybe they always go to a certain dresser or trunk in their room. Place it somewhere they go to regularly. This way, they can open it up and enjoy it even when you are not around.

4. Start keeping tabs. The idea here is to create a book that captures phone calls, visitors, and inquiries about your family member. This part of the process may be your responsibility. However, if your family member is able, guide them in adding to the book and creating entries. Our suggestion would be to date each entry (as in a diary or journal) and write a few sentences about what was talked about during each visit or phone call. Maybe you can include what you laughed about! This is not to check up on people or to keep score. The point is simply to remind your family member that they are loved. Visitors can also write entries when they come to see your loved one.

5. Create a guestbook day every week. Make an activity out of this. Pick up your loved one's favorite snack, find a quiet place, and then sit down together and go through the week's contacts. Read to your family member about the week's visitors and phone calls. If they forgot, this informs them!

TIPS

- If your family member lives in a facility (nursing home, assisted living, etc.), do not abandon this activity quite yet. Perhaps you can recruit some help from some of the staff at the facility to help you keep track of the contacts. They do not have to listen in on phone conversations, but possibly they can jot down when someone called and visited to the best of their knowledge. The staff is often aware of these things, especially if your family member does not have their own phone.

- If your family member lives alone in their own home, place a notepad next to the phone in a place that they cannot miss. Write something that would cue them to keep track of their own phone calls, such as a note reminding them to write down the name of the person who called and leave blank space for them to jot it down. You can write headings (name of caller, topic of conversation, etc.) that will walk them through the information, and you can help them put the information into the guestbook later.

- This activity can serve multiple purposes. Besides being a reminder of all those who care, it can also serve as an anxiety buffer. If your family member is ever upset or anxious because they think that no one visits or calls, you can pull out their guestbook to show them and hopefully calm their anxieties.

Increase the challenge by creating a fancy book.

ADAPTATIONS

More Challenging

- To make this activity more challenging, you can have your family member not only work on their own book, but possibly help someone else create one as well. This not only adds steps to the project, which in turn adds complexity, but it also allows them to feel good about helping someone else.

- You can also add more challenge to this activity by having your family member initiate new entries. Rather than have them waiting around for someone to call or visit, have them call others. Perhaps once a week they can call someone and add the entry to the book. There is no rule saying that they have to wait around for calls and visits!

- You can also increase the challenge by creating a fancy book. Instead of using the standard notebook or the loose-leaf sheets stored in a binder, decorate the cover, decorate the pages, etc. Add pizzazz to the book, and have your family member help you if they can.

Less Challenging

Just talk about visitors who came that week.

- If you like the idea of this activity, but are concerned that your family member will not recognize the names that appear in the entries, we can remedy that by creating a bio page. In the front of the book, add pages of pictures of all who would be calling or visiting. Below their photo, put their name, relationship, and something about them. For example, put in a picture of your loved one's granddaughter. Underneath her picture, you can write, "This is my granddaughter, Kate. Kate loves ponies. She is in the 5th grade and calls me every Wednesday." That way, if your family member does not remember who a particular caller was, you can turn to the front page of your book and refresh their memory with the picture.

- You can also decrease the complexity by eliminating the idea of the guestbook, but keep the same general concept. Go to a quiet place once a week with their favorite snack, and just talk about visitors and who came that week.

- Eliminate the idea of the guestbook, and help your family member call someone on the phone every week. Have the picture of the person you're calling in front of your family member when you do this.

Food Drive

DESCRIPTION

It feels good to help others. It is particularly rewarding when the people that you help are really in need. This next activity allows your family member to experience that pride of helping others in need with the expectation of nothing in return. How many people out there need food, but can afford little? How would you feel if you, along with the help of your family member, have your own family food drive? This activity can make that happen.

HOW TO

It feels good to help others.

1. The first step is to get a big plastic bin (such as a laundry basket) or cardboard box that you can place in a central location. Make a sign for the bin or box that says, "Place Food for Donation Here." The label serves as a visual cue or reminder of the activity in case your family member forgets. If they can help make the label, that's even better. Although this big plastic or cardboard obstruction may be an eye sore in your home for a period of time, it is for a great cause and well worth the sacrifice. If your family member lives in a facility, perhaps you could talk to a staff member about borrowing some space for a month or so to place a bin or box for food. You still want to make a sign for it. This food drive would now be extended to others in the facility, such as other residents and their families as well as staff. What a wonderful thing for you and your loved one to start up!

2. The second step is to start collecting the food. This gives you a reason to clean out your cupboards. Involve your family member in this process as much as possible. If they live at home with you, bring them to the kitchen with you as you clear out the cupboards. Place boxes or cans in their hands. Let them hold things or place things in piles. If your family member lives in a facility, pack some canned goods up in a box and bring it with you when you visit so you can go through the box together. If at all possible, take your family member on a weekly trip to a discounted grocery store or even your local grocery store and pick up a new can or two a week. Make them a part of this.

3. Continue to add to your box or bin of food until it is full. Once it is full, you have the option of continuing to collect more and starting another box or bin, or bring the food to a hunger center in your area. If it is possible for your family member to be there with you when you make the delivery to the hunger center, that would be great. Have them share in this experience. It is a truly rewarding one.

TIPS

- If you do not know of a hunger center in your area or cannot find one in the phonebook, a good resource is a neighborhood church or temple. They often do work to benefit those that are less fortunate and may be familiar with the hunger centers in or around the area. They may even collect food themselves to donate.

ADAPTATIONS

More Challenging

Have your loved ones sort the foods that you plan to donate.

- To make this activity more of a challenge, you can have your family member do more. Give them a box of food from your cupboards and allow them to pick and choose what they think should be donated on their own.

- Another way to increase the complexity is to have them sort the foods that you plan to donate, such as canned vegetables, boxed pastas, etc. This adds categorizing and sorting to the task. You can also have a different box for each category and have them create labels for the categories. This way, the donation center can just read the labels on the boxes to know what is inside of each box.

Less Challenging

- You can reduce the complexity of this activity by reducing the amount of time that you carry it on. Collect until your one box or bin is full. Collect for a week. Collect for a couple of days. It really doesn't matter. This is still an engaging activity that you are participating in with the assistance of your loved one. You can also have your family member take more of a passive role in the process. Instead of physically helping with the food selection or holding any cans or putting anything in boxes, they can simply observe and you can talk to them about what you are doing. They are still a part of the process, a process that results in extending a hand to others who are less fortunate. You can also just give them one single role of placing items in the box or bin. If need be, you can even do everything and just take them with you to drop the food off at the hunger center.

Charity Walk

DESCRIPTION

When we think of charity walks, we typically do not envision older adults as the participants. We assume that the physical aspect of the walk may be too demanding for them. But if you really think about it, why can't they participate? Who says you have to finish the walk? Who says you can't just be there to watch? The older adults that we know are often as strong in will, heart, and mind as many of the typical charity walk participants. Would you be interested in participating, along side your older loved one, and do your part in supporting a good cause.

HOW TO

1. Check with your family member's physician to be sure it's alright for them to participate. If your family member's health would not allow them to participate comfortably and safely, try another activity.

2. The second step is to choose the walk. Look into ones that are up and coming. Pay attention to the distance, time of day, and locations of the walks, and determine whether they are options for you and your family member. There are many charity walks out there that benefit so many different causes, such as diabetes, breast cancer, multiple sclerosis, AIDS, Alzheimer's disease, hunger, etc. Perhaps you could choose one that has touched someone that you or your family member knows. This would make it a personal experience for you. Discuss the different options with your loved one. Allow them to give some feedback in terms of the walk choices.

Support your favorite cause!

3. Once you have made a decision about the particular walk that you would like to do, research the entry requirements. You can probably register on the spot, but they usually have pre-registration as well. Pre-registration would allow you to get your t-shirt, hat, or bag (whatever they give out) in advance and wear it the day of the walk. You would be showing your support before you even took one step.

Attend the walk and cheer on other participants.

4. Make a decision about your loved one's level of participation. In what capacity do you think that they are capable of participating? Are they strong enough to actually walk one of the smaller one-mile walks? Would you feel more comfortable with them in a wheelchair? Can they walk some and then stop? Make a general decision about their participation level. This does not have to be etched in stone. If the day of the walk comes and they are feeling strong and energized, perhaps they could walk a little further than you had planned. If not, perhaps they could at least watch. Once you have made this decision, plan accordingly. If you are going to transport them in a wheelchair, make sure that their wheelchair is ready to roll.

5. When walk day approaches, attend! Do your part to support the cause.

TIPS

- Be realistic. We are not expecting your family member to put on their cross-country shoes and run two miles. We are not even expecting your family member to walk two miles. They can walk two feet and that would be perfectly acceptable. If they have to be pushed in a wheelchair for two miles, then they have to be pushed in a wheelchair. They are there at the walk and showing their support to the cause. They are taking in the surroundings and being a part of the whole experience.

- Watch the weather reports a few days before the walk. Be aware of what lies ahead in terms of precipitation and temperature. If it is an extremely hot or cold day, or if it is raining, the walk may not be feasible. Use good judgment. Do not leave home without water for hydration.

ADAPTATIONS

More Challenging

- Help your family member secure some sponsors.

- If it is safe to do this, you can also hold practice sessions before the big walk. Have your family member walk short distances first. This will not only help them prepare for the walk, but it will create more to do, thus increasing the complexity of this project.

Less Challenging

- If the idea of participating in a charity walk is appealing, but you truly do not feel comfortable having your loved one actually walk due to their health, then let's discuss other alternatives. You can attend the walk and cheer on the other participants without actually participating physically. The energy at these walks is something fascinating to see. Many of the people participating have been afflicted with the condition or know someone that has struggled with the condition that is the theme of the walk. The strength and image of these people fighting together for the same cause is powerful.

- You can also make a donation to the foundation sponsoring the walk. This does not require you to even attend the walk. Simply make a donation to the cause. This is still showing support. You can also make a donation to a church or temple in memory of someone who has lost their life as a result of one of these conditions.

- Another option is for you and your family member to walk a certain distance within their facility, if they live in one, or around their block if they live in their home? For example, you could walk with your family member or push them in their wheelchair four times up and down a hall each visit until they have reached their distance goal. Have them wear a tee shirt or hat of the sponsoring event while you are walking with them. After they finish, make a field trip out of delivering a monetary donation to the sponsoring agency.

- Have a discussion about the different charitable organizations. Your family member may not be familiar with what they are doing.

- You can also discuss a way for your family to do something together to help the cause, whether it's a prayer, a day of volunteering, or sponsoring another walker, such as a grandchild.

The energy at these walks is something fascinating to see.

Becoming a Volunteer

DESCRIPTION

Older adults have so much to share. How do you feel about helping your family member to give a little of their time to others? This activity is about you and your family member participating in a volunteer program together. If your loved one was ever involved in community service, this may be a great opportunity to become involved all over again.

Older adults have so much to share.

HOW TO

1. The first step to this activity is to do some research. Look into volunteer programs that are available in your area. Are there any libraries or daycare centers that have volunteers read stories to children? Another option is to look into volunteer opportunities with other older adults. Are there any day programs, nursing homes, or senior centers that welcome older volunteers?

2. Contact some potential places that offer volunteer opportunities. Ask some questions. See what types of programs that they offer and what types of volunteers that they are looking for. Programs specifically for senior citizens or families may already be out there.

3. Narrow down the selection to two choices. Bring the choices to your loved one and ask for their input.

4. Commit to a program.

TIPS

- The only tip that we have is to do this together with your family member. We would never suggest that you should try to arrange this for your family member to do alone. Let the agency know that your family member has memory difficulties, but that you will be with them and responsible for them. We realize that this may not be a good idea for some people. Luckily, there are many other activities to choose from!

- When you actually begin your program, use these volunteer opportunities as excuses to do something else special as well, such as going on a lunch outing. Every time that you go to volunteer, you can take your loved one out to lunch first or to a coffee shop. This makes a whole special day out of your volunteer opportunity and gives both of you something to look forward to.

Create your own volunteer program.

ADAPTATIONS

More Challenging

- Create your own volunteer program for your family member and a grandchild or a family friend. Once a week or once a month, plan a special activity day for you, your family member, and the child(ren). Planning the special activity day can be a whole activity in and of itself for you and your loved one. For example, you could plan a story-time hour. To prepare for the story time festivities, you could take your family member to the library to pick out a book in the children's section.

- You could bring out lemonade and cookies after the story has been read to make for a happy ending. You can choose whatever would be fun and of interest.

- See if your family member would like to join a residents' council or committee if they live in a long-term care facility.

Less Challenging

- Volunteer less frequently. Rather than commit to volunteering once a month, for example, volunteer every three months.

- Your family member can do some volunteer work in the comfort of their own home. You can check with charitable organizations in the area and see if they have any flyers that need to be folded or stuffed in envelopes. Or, you can have your loved one help you with something at home. If it is around the holiday time, possibly they can help you with your holiday cards by putting on return address labels, stamps, or stuffing the cards in envelopes. Perhaps they could make a flower arrangement to give to someone who is ill.

Toys for Kids

DESCRIPTION

The holiday season is supposed to be a fun, festive, and joyous time of the year. However, for people that do not have families, it can actually be a sad time. With this next activity, you and your loved one can reach out and help to make some less fortunate children a little happier during the holidays.

HOW TO

1. The idea behind this activity is collecting toys for disadvantaged children. Your first step is to investigate the different options for donating in your area. You will also want to call and talk to someone to make sure that they take donations from the general public. Then, narrow the options down to two. Present the two charitable options to your loved one and have them help you make the final decision.

Reach out to less fortunate children during the holidays.

2. Now your search for toys can begin. We are not suggesting spending lots of money on these toys. This is also an activity that should be spread out over a few weeks or months. Extending this activity gives you and your family member a project to focus on together for a period of time, but it also helps in terms of money because you are not spending it all at once. Take your family member with you to shop for toys, if you can. Allow them to pick out some of the toys. If their health does not permit them to come with you, show them all of your purchases and see what they think of them.

3. Children love opening gifts. However, disadvantaged children may not receive a lot of presents, which means that they may not have the opportunity to open gift bags or boxes too often. If it's an option, package the toys up, gift-style. We would suggest using a gift bag instead of wrapping paper because it may be easier for your family member to work with a bag rather than wrapping paper. Gift bags can get quite costly, but you do not have to buy the fancy ones. Plain colored paper gift bags would work just fine. Stuff the gift bag with plain white tissue paper, nothing fancy. For smaller gifts, there are cellophane bags that are often sold in packages of 30 or so. They even have them at dollar stores.

   You may want to begin packaging your toys up as they are purchased. Perhaps you can sit down with your family member once a week and have a "gift night." Make some hot chocolate, put on the holiday music, and prepare the children's gift bags.

4. Set a collection end-date. The holiday time is obviously busy for everyone and you have to prepare for your own holiday festivities. Therefore, set a final date and when that date arrives, stop with what you have, package any un-bagged gifts, and prepare for the final step: delivery.

5. If your family member is at all able, take them with you to deliver these presents. Even if you could not hand the presents out directly to the children, just seeing the faces of children may bring some smiles.

Use gift bags instead of wrapping paper.

TIPS

- If you choose to donate to a facility, ask how many children are there. If the numbers are small, make sure to have enough presents for each child to receive at least one.

ADAPTATIONS

More Challenging

- Eliminate the idea of the gift bags and wrap the presents instead. You could even wrap them in newspaper to keep the cost down. Add a bow as an additional step.

- Have your family member help you create gift tags, custom-made gift cards or even help decorate the gift bags.

- Personalize the gifts more. Instead of buying random toys, try to find out a little about the children's personal interests. Ask someone at the place where you will make your donations. After you find out about the children's interests, try to find toys that relate to them.

Less Challenging

- Donate a single toy.

Family members can watch as you wrap gifts.

- Your family member can watch you as you gift wrap the toy, and the two of you can talk about the donation.

- If your family member cannot come with you to drop off the toys, tell them afterwards about the reactions of the children.

NOTES

NOTES

NOTES

NOTES